2017 SQA Specimen and Past Papers with Answers

National 5

BIOLOGY

National 5 BIOLOGY

2016 & 2017 Exams
and 2017 Specimen Question Paper

HODDER GIBSON
AN HACHETTE UK COMPANY

This book contains the official SQA 2016 and 2017 Exams, and the 2017 Specimen Question Paper for National 5 Biology, with associated SQA-approved answers modified from the official marking instructions that accompany the paper.

In addition the book contains study skills advice. This has been specially commissioned by Hodder Gibson, and has been written by experienced senior teachers and examiners in line with the new National 5 syllabus and assessment outlines. This is not SQA material but has been devised to provide further guidance for National 5 examinations.

Hodder Gibson is grateful to the copyright holders, as credited on the final page of the Answer section, for permission to use their material. Every effort has been made to trace the copyright holders and to obtain their permission for the use of copyright material. Hodder Gibson will be happy to receive information allowing us to rectify any error or omission in future editions.

Hachette UK's policy is to use papers that are natural, renewable and recyclable products and made from wood grown in sustainable forests. The logging and manufacturing processes are expected to conform to the environmental regulations of the country of origin.

Orders: please contact Bookpoint Ltd, 130 Park Drive, Milton Park, Abingdon, Oxon OX14 4SE. Telephone: (44) 01235 827720. Fax: (44) 01235 400454. Lines are open 9.00–5.00, Monday to Saturday, with a 24-hour message answering service. Visit our website at www.hoddereducation.co.uk. Hodder Gibson can be contacted direct on: Tel: 0141 333 4650; Fax: 0141 404 8188; email: hoddergibson@hodder.co.uk

This collection first published in 2017 by
Hodder Gibson, an imprint of Hodder Education,
An Hachette UK Company
211 St Vincent Street
Glasgow G2 5QY

Typeset by Aptara, Inc.

Printed in the UK

A catalogue record for this title is available from the British Library

ISBN: 978-1-5104-2157-8

2 1

2018 2017

MIX
Paper from
responsible sources
FSC™ C104740
FSC
www.fsc.org

Introduction

National 5 Biology

This book of SQA past papers contains the question papers used in the 2016 and 2017 exams (with answers at the back of the book). The National 5 Biology exam is being extended by 20 marks for 2018 onwards, following the removal of unit assessments from the course. A new specimen question paper, which reflects the requirements of the revised exam, is also included. The specimen question paper reflects the content and duration of the exam in 2018.

All of the question papers included in the book (2016, 2017 and the new specimen question paper) provide excellent representative exam practice for the final exams. Using the 2016 and 2017 past papers as part of your revision will help you to develop the vital skills and techniques needed for the exam, and will help you to identify any knowledge gaps you may have.

It is always a very good idea to refer to SQA's website for the most up-to-date course specification documents. These are available for each subject at www.sqa.org.uk/nqsubjects

The Course

The National 5 Biology Course consists of three areas of biology. These are *Cell Biology*, *Multicellular Organisms* and *Life on Earth*. In each of the areas you will be assessed on your ability to demonstrate and apply knowledge of Biology, and to demonstrate and apply skills of scientific inquiry. Candidates complete an Assignment in which they investigate and research a topic in biology and write it up as a report. They also take a Course Examination.

How the Course is graded

The grade you get for National 5 Biology depends on the following two Course assessments, which are set and graded by SQA.

1 An **Assignment** in which candidates spend up to 8 hours investigating and researching a biological topic and producing a written report under exam conditions. The Assignment makes up 20% of your grade and is marked out of 20 marks, most of which are allocated for skills of scientific inquiry.

2 A written **Course Examination**, which is worth the remaining 80% of the grade. The Examination is marked out of 100 marks, most of which are for the demonstration and application of knowledge, although there are also marks available for skills of scientific inquiry. This book should help you practise the Examination part!

To pass National 5 Biology with a C grade you will need about 50% of the 120 marks available for the Assignment and the Course Examination combined. For a B, you will need 60%, and for an A, 70%.

The Course Examination

The Course Examination is a single question paper split into two sections. The first section is an objective test with 25 multiple choice items for 25 marks. The second section is a mixture of restricted and extended response questions worth between 1 and 4 marks each for a total of 75 marks. Some questions will contain options and there will usually be a question that asks you to suggest changes to experimental methods. Altogether there are 80 marks, and you will have two and a half hours to complete the paper. Most of the marks are for knowledge and its application, with the remainder of questions designed to test skills of scientific inquiry.

The majority of the marks will be straightforward – these are the marks that will help you get a grade C. Some questions will be more demanding – these are the questions you need to get right to get a grade A.

General hints and tips

You should have a copy of the Course Specification for National 5 Biology – if you haven't got one, download it from the SQA website. This document tells you what you may be tested on in your examination. It is worth spending some time studying this document.

This book contains three question papers. The final paper is a specimen paper that shows exactly how the examination question paper will be constructed. The first two papers are past papers from 2016 and 2017. Although these are very similar to the examination question paper, they only have 80 marks each overall. They still represent very good practice for your exam. Make sure that you spend time checking your answers using the answer section – it is useful if you can get someone to help you with this.

NB. There are a very small number of marks in the 2016 (Paper 2, Q3b, 2 marks) and 2017 (Paper 2, Q14a/c, 3 marks) papers that will no longer be appropriate for the N5 specification as the learning outcomes they test have been deleted.

If you are trying a whole examination paper from this book, give yourself a maximum of two and a half hours to complete it. Make sure that you spend time using the answer section to mark your own work – it is especially useful if you can get someone to help you with this. You could even grade your work on an A–D basis.

The following hints and tips are related to examination techniques as well as avoiding common mistakes.

Remember that if you hit problems with a question, you should ask your teacher for help.

Section 1

25 multiple-choice items 25 marks

- Answer on the grid provided.
- Do not spend more than about **40 minutes** on this section.
- Some individual questions might take longer to answer than others – this is quite normal and make sure you use scrap paper if a calculation or any working is needed.
- Some questions can be answered instantly – again, this is normal.
- **Do not leave blanks** – complete the grid for each question as you work through.
- Try to answer each question in your head **without** looking at the options. If your answer is there – you are home and dry!
- If you are not certain, choose the answer that seemed most attractive on **first** reading the answer options.
- If you are guessing, try to eliminate options before making your guess. If you can eliminate 3 – you are left with the correct answer even if you do not recognise it!

Section 2

Restricted and extended response 75 marks

- Spend about **110 minutes** on this section.
- Answer on the question paper. Try to write neatly and keep your answers on the support lines if possible – the lines are designed to take the full answer!
- A clue to answer length is the mark allocation – most questions are restricted to 1 mark and the answer can be quite short. If there are 2–4 marks available, your answer will need to be extended and may well have two, three or even four parts.
- The parts of each question usually test a single Key Area or set of scientific inquiry skills but remember some questions are **designed** to cover more than one Key Area.
- The grade C-type questions usually start with "**State**", "**Identify**", "**Give**" or "**Name**" and often need only a word or two in response. They will usually be worth one mark each.
- Questions that begin with "**Explain**", "**Suggest**" or "**Describe**" are usually grade A types and are likely to have more than one part to the full answer. You will usually have to write a sentence or two and there may be two or even three marks available.
- Questions that begin with "**Calculate**" will need some numerical working and will have a space left for this. Although it is recommended that you show working, it is not necessary to do so to score the marks.
- Make sure you read questions through twice before trying to answer – there is often very important information within the question.
- Using abbreviations like DNA and ATP is fine, and the bases of DNA can be given as A, T, G and C.
- Don't worry that a few questions are in unfamiliar contexts – that's the idea! Just keep calm and read the questions carefully.
- If a question contains a choice, be sure to spend a minute or two making the best choice for you. You will probably need to circle your choice – make sure you do so.
- In experimental questions, you must be aware of what variables are, why controls are needed and how reliability might be improved. It is worth spending time on these ideas – they are essential and will come up year after year.
- Some candidates like to use a highlighter pen to help them focus on the essential points of longer questions – this is a great technique.
- Remember that a **conclusion** can be seen from data, whereas an **explanation** will usually require you to supply some background knowledge as well.
- If you are asked to write a conclusion from experimental data, remember to relate it to the aim of the experiment.
- Remember to "**use values from the graph**" when describing graphical information in words if you are asked to do so.
- Complete graphs and charts neatly and carefully using a ruler for the tops of bars, pie chart sections and to connect points on line graphs. Include zeros on your scale where appropriate and use the data table headings for the axes labels. For line graphs, join the plot points with straight lines using a ruler. For bar charts use a ruler for the tops on the bars and in pie charts use a ruler for the sections.

- Look out for graphs with two Y axes – these need extra special concentration and anyone can make a mistake!
- If you are given space for a calculation you will very likely need to use it! A calculator is essential.
- The main types of calculation tend to be **ratios**, **averages** and **percentages** – make sure you can do these common calculations.
- Answers to calculations will not usually have more than two decimal places.
- Do not leave blanks. Always have a go, using the language in the question if you can.

Good luck!

Remember that the rewards for passing National 5 Biology are well worth it! Your pass will help you get the future you want for yourself. In the exam, be confident in your own ability. If you're not sure how to answer a question, trust your instincts and just give it a go anyway. Keep calm and don't panic! GOOD LUCK!

Study Skills – what you need to know to pass exams!

Pause for thought

Many students might skip quickly through a page like this. After all, we all know how to revise. Do you really though?

Think about this:

"IF YOU ALWAYS DO WHAT YOU ALWAYS DO, YOU WILL ALWAYS GET WHAT YOU HAVE ALWAYS GOT."

Do you like the grades you get? Do you want to do better? If you get full marks in your assessment, then that's great! Change nothing! This section is just to help you get that little bit better than you already are.

There are two main parts to the advice on offer here. The first part highlights fairly obvious things but which are also very important. The second part makes suggestions about revision that you might not have thought about but which WILL help you.

Part 1

DOH! It's so obvious but ...

Start revising in good time

Don't leave it until the last minute – this will make you panic.

Make a revision timetable that sets out work time AND play time.

Sleep and eat!

Obvious really, and very helpful. Avoid arguments or stressful things too – even games that wind you up. You need to be fit, awake and focused!

Know your place!

Make sure you know exactly **WHEN and WHERE** your exams are.

Know your enemy!

Make sure you know what to expect in the exam.

How is the paper structured?

How much time is there for each question?

What types of question are involved?

Which topics seem to come up time and time again?

Which topics are your strongest and which are your weakest?

Are all topics compulsory or are there choices?

Learn by DOING!

There is no substitute for past papers and practice papers – they are simply essential! Tackling this collection of papers and answers is exactly the right thing to be doing as your exams approach.

Part 2

People learn in different ways. Some like low light, some bright. Some like early morning, some like evening / night. Some prefer warm, some prefer cold. But everyone uses their BRAIN and the brain works when it is active. Passive learning – sitting gazing at notes – is the most INEFFICIENT way to learn anything. Below you will find tips and ideas for making your revision more effective and maybe even more enjoyable. What follows gets your brain active, and active learning works!

Activity 1 – Stop and review

Step 1

When you have done no more than 5 minutes of revision reading STOP!

Step 2

Write a heading in your own words which sums up the topic you have been revising.

Step 3

Write a summary of what you have revised in no more than two sentences. Don't fool yourself by saying, "I know it, but I cannot put it into words". That just means you don't know it well enough. If you cannot write your summary, revise that section again, knowing that you must write a summary at the end of it. Many of you will have notebooks full of blue/black ink writing. Many of the pages will not be especially attractive or memorable so try to liven them up a bit with colour as you are reviewing and rewriting. **This is a great memory aid, and memory is the most important thing.**

Activity 2 – Use technology!

Why should everything be written down? Have you thought about "mental" maps, diagrams, cartoons and colour to help you learn? And rather than write down notes, why not record your revision material?

What about having a text message revision session with friends? Keep in touch with them to find out how and what they are revising and share ideas and questions.

Why not make a video diary where you tell the camera what you are doing, what you think you have learned and what you still have to do? No one has to see or hear it, but the process of having to organise your thoughts in a formal way to explain something is a very important learning practice.

Be sure to make use of electronic files. You could begin to summarise your class notes. Your typing might be slow, but it will get faster and the typed notes will be easier to read than the scribbles in your class notes. Try to add different fonts and colours to make your work stand out. You can easily Google relevant pictures, cartoons and diagrams which you can copy and paste to make your work more attractive and **MEMORABLE**.

Activity 3 – This is it. Do this and you will know lots!

Step 1

In this task you must be very honest with yourself! Find the SQA syllabus for your subject (www.sqa.org.uk). Look at how it is broken down into main topics called MANDATORY knowledge. That means stuff you MUST know.

Step 2

BEFORE you do ANY revision on this topic, write a list of everything that you already know about the subject. It might be quite a long list but you only need to write it once. It shows you all the information that is already in your long-term memory so you know what parts you do not need to revise!

Step 3

Pick a chapter or section from your book or revision notes. Choose a fairly large section or a whole chapter to get the most out of this activity.

With a buddy, use Skype, Facetime, Twitter or any other communication you have, to play the game "If this is the answer, what is the question?". For example, if you are revising Geography and the answer you provide is "meander", your buddy would have to make up a question like "What is the word that describes a feature of a river where it flows slowly and bends often from side to side?".

Make up 10 "answers" based on the content of the chapter or section you are using. Give this to your buddy to solve while you solve theirs.

Step 4

Construct a wordsearch of at least 10 × 10 squares. You can make it as big as you like but keep it realistic. Work together with a group of friends. Many apps allow you to make wordsearch puzzles online. The words and phrases can go in any direction and phrases can be split. Your puzzle must only contain facts linked to the topic you are revising. Your task is to find 10 bits of information to hide in your puzzle, but you must not repeat information that you used in Step 3. DO NOT show where the words are. Fill up empty squares with random letters. Remember to keep a note of where your answers are hidden but do not show your friends. When you have a complete puzzle, exchange it with a friend to solve each other's puzzle.

Step 5

Now make up 10 questions (not "answers" this time) based on the same chapter used in the previous two tasks. Again, you must find NEW information that you have not yet used. Now it's getting hard to find that new information! Again, give your questions to a friend to answer.

Step 6

As you have been doing the puzzles, your brain has been actively searching for new information. Now write a NEW LIST that contains only the new information you have discovered when doing the puzzles. Your new list is the one to look at repeatedly for short bursts over the next few days. Try to remember more and more of it without looking at it. After a few days, you should be able to add words from your second list to your first list as you increase the information in your long-term memory.

FINALLY! Be inspired...

Make a list of different revision ideas and beside each one write **THINGS I HAVE** tried, **THINGS I WILL** try and **THINGS I MIGHT** try. Don't be scared of trying something new.

And remember – "FAIL TO PREPARE AND PREPARE TO FAIL!"

NATIONAL 5

2016

SQA ©

HODDER GIBSON
LEARN MORE

N5 National Qualifications 2016

X707/75/02

Biology
Section 1—Questions

MONDAY, 9 MAY

1:00 PM – 3:00 PM

Instructions for the completion of Section 1 are given on *Page two* of your question and answer booklet X707/75/01.

Record your answers on the answer grid on *Page three* of your question and answer booklet

Before leaving the examination room you must give your question and answer booklet to the Invigilator; if you do not, you may lose all the marks for this paper.

SECTION 1

1. The diagram below shows parts of a plant cell.

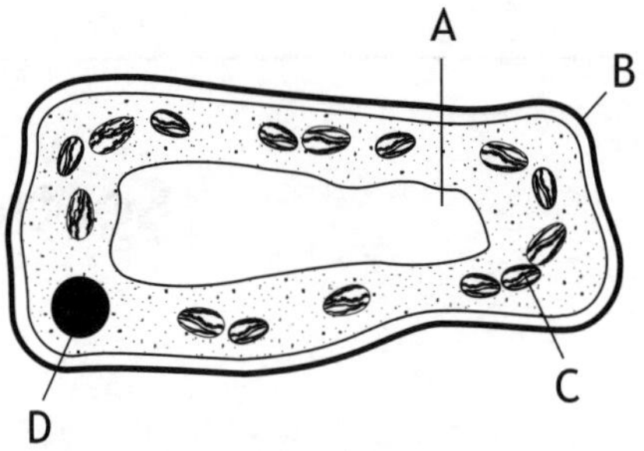

Which part of this cell is composed of cellulose?

2. Four cylinders of potato tissue were weighed and each was placed into a salt solution of a different concentration.

The cylinders were reweighed after one hour and the results are shown below.

Salt Solution	*Initial mass of potato cylinder* (g)	*Final mass of potato cylinder* (g)
A	10·0	7·0
B	10·0	9·4
C	10·0	11·2
D	10·0	12·6

In which salt solution would most potato cells be plasmolysed?

3. The diagram below shows the percentage of cells dividing in four areas of an onion root.

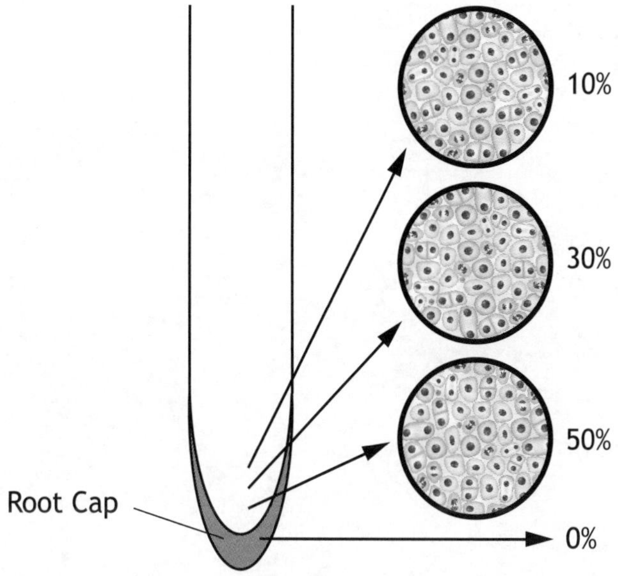

Which graph represents the number of cells dividing in this root?

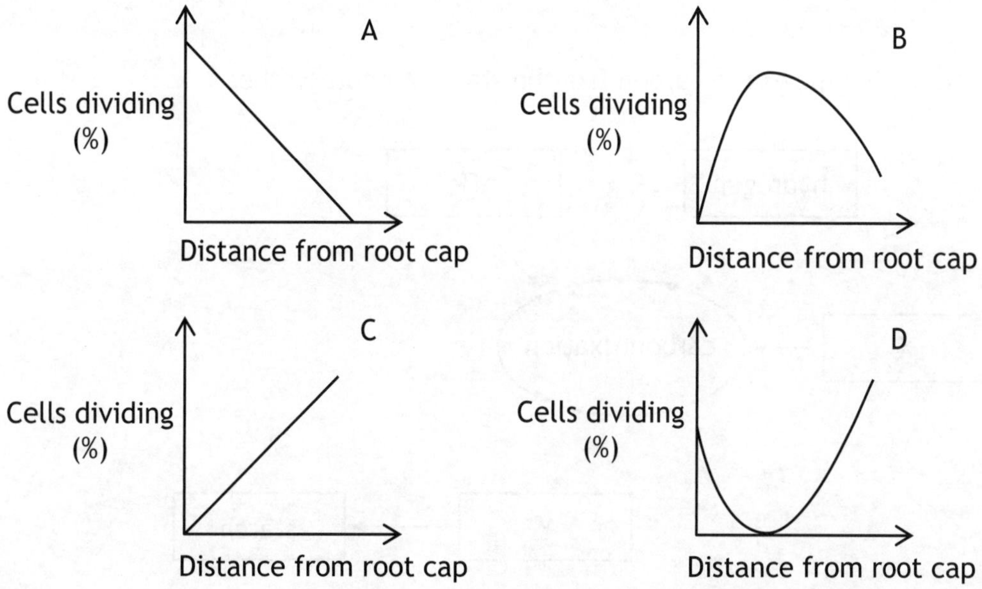

[Turn over

4. Which of the following shows the correct DNA base pairing?

A
A - C
C - G
G - C
T - A

B
A - T
C - G
G - T
T - A

C
A - G
C - G
G - A
T - A

D
A - T
C - G
G - C
T - A

5. Hormones are composed of

A glycerol
B glucose
C protein
D starch.

6. The diagram below shows the carbon fixation stage of photosynthesis.

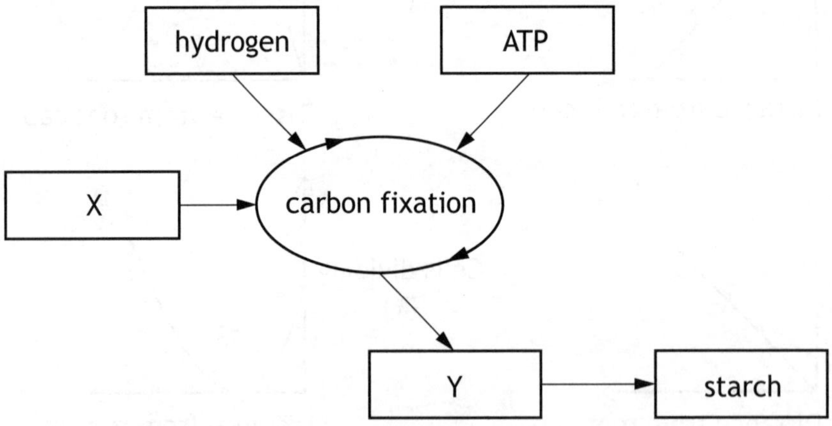

Which row in the table below identifies X and Y?

	X	*Y*
A	Sugar	Oxygen
B	Water	Carbon dioxide
C	Carbon dioxide	Sugar
D	Water	Oxygen

7. An investigation was carried out to compare the rate of oxygen gas production by two different species of water plant, S and T.

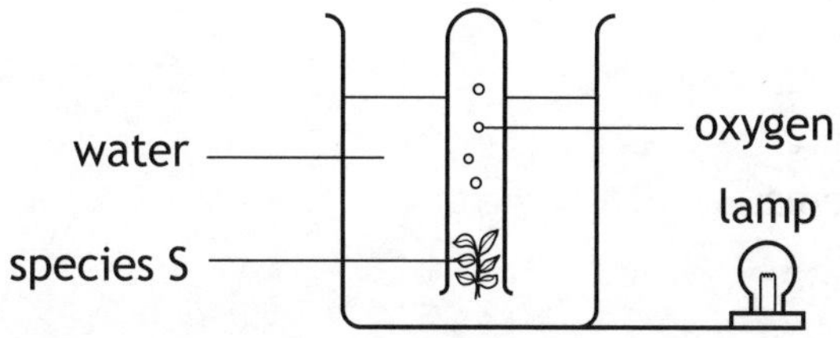

Which diagram below shows the set-up for species T, that would allow a valid comparison in the rate of oxygen production of the two species?

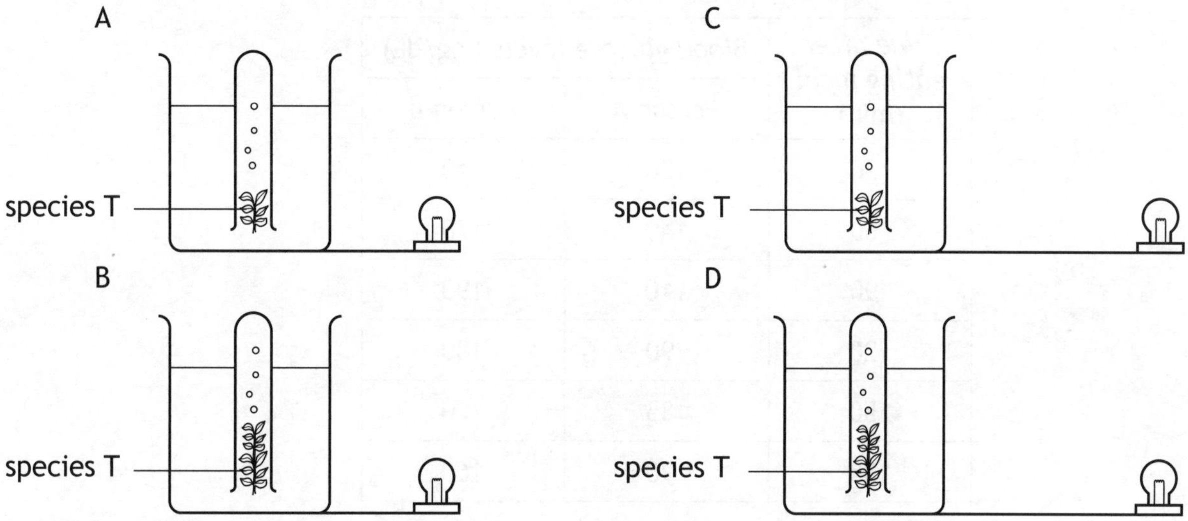

8. Each skin cell in a mouse has 40 chromosomes. How many chromosomes were present in each cell after dividing four times during cell culture?

A 10

B 20

C 40

D 160

[Turn over

9. Specialisation of cells in animals leads to the formation of

A tissues and organs

B meristems and organs

C stem cells and tissues

D stem cells and meristems.

10. The table below shows the blood glucose levels of two people after eating the same meal.

The normal range of blood glucose levels is 82–110 mg/dL.

Time after eating meal (min)	*Blood glucose levels* (mg/dL)	
	Person A	*Person B*
30	120	140
60	140	170
90	110	190
120	90	180
150	85	170
180	90	160

Using the information given, which of the following statements is correct?

A Person A always stayed within the normal range.

B Person B was outwith the normal range 180 minutes after eating.

C Person B had a level twice as high as that of person A 180 minutes after eating.

D Person A and person B both had their highest levels 90 minutes after eating.

11. The diagram below shows the structure of a flower.

Where are the male gametes produced?

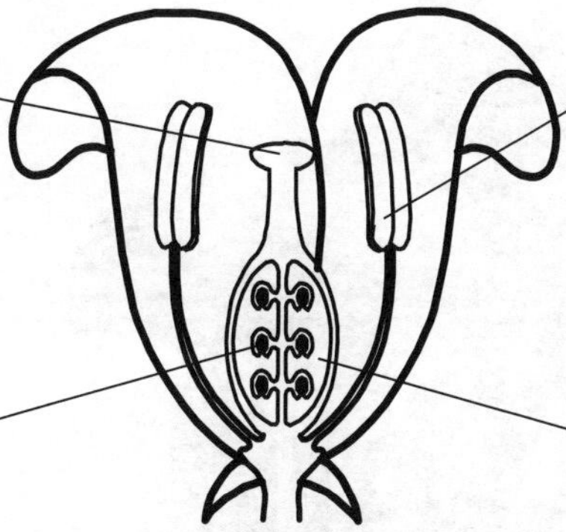

12. Most features of an individual phenotype are

A controlled by a single gene and show continuous variation

B controlled by a single gene and show discrete variation

C polygenic and show continuous variation

D polygenic and show discrete variation.

13. The following diagram shows the inheritance of coat colour in guinea pigs.

P Phenotype	Black guinea pig	X	White guinea pig
P Genotype:	BB		bb
F1 Genotype:		Bb	
F2 Genotypes:		BB and Bb and bb	

Which of the following generations contain heterozygous individuals?

A P and F1

B P and F2

C F1 and F2

D P, F1 and F2

[Turn over

14. The diagram below shows the heart and associated blood vessels.

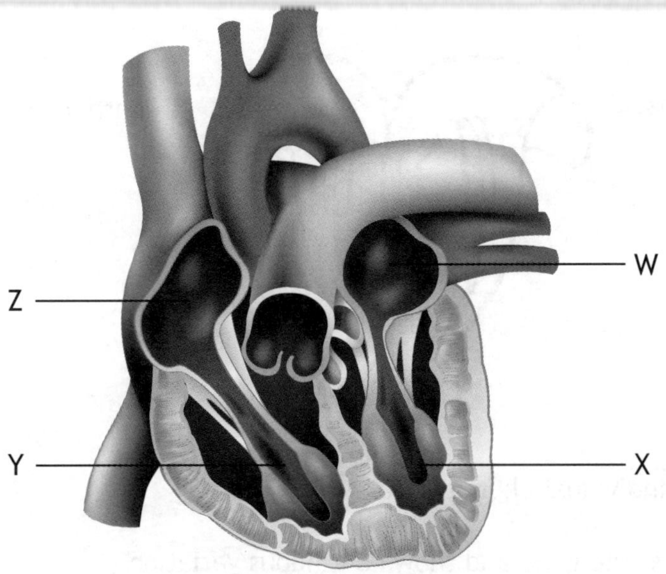

Which of the following statements is correct?

A W is the left atrium which receives blood from the body.

B X is the left ventricle which pumps blood to the body.

C Y is the right atrium which receives blood from the lungs.

D Z is the right ventricle which pumps blood to the lungs.

15. Which of the following statements best describes a niche?

A A living factor which affects biodiversity in an ecosystem.

B A region of our planet as distinguished by its climate, fauna and flora.

C All the organisms in an area and their habitat.

D The role that an organism plays within a community.

16. An ecosystem receives 6 000 000 units of energy from the sun.

Of this energy, 95% is **not** used in photosynthesis.

The amount of energy captured by the producers in this ecosystem is

A 30 000

B 300 000

C 570 000

D 5 700 000.

17. The graph below shows changes in the population of red and grey squirrels in an area of woodland over a 10 year period.

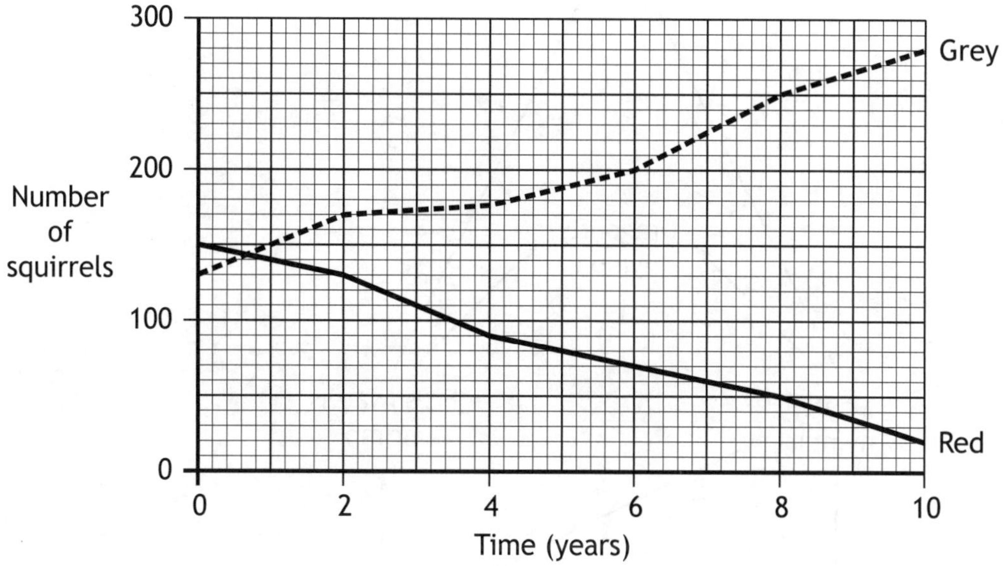

Which of the following conclusions can be drawn from the graph?

A The total number of squirrels decreased over 10 years.

B The population of red squirrels showed a greater change than the grey squirrels.

C The population of grey squirrels showed a greater change than the red squirrels.

D After 8 years there were 4 times as many grey squirrels as red squirrels.

18. Which of the following is a source of new alleles in a population?

A Mutation

B Isolation

C Natural selection

D Environmental conditions

19. Indicator species can provide information about

A numbers of organisms in a lake

B numbers of predators in a woodland

C levels of light in an ecosystem

D levels of pollution in a river.

[Turn over

20. The diagram below represents a freshwater food web.

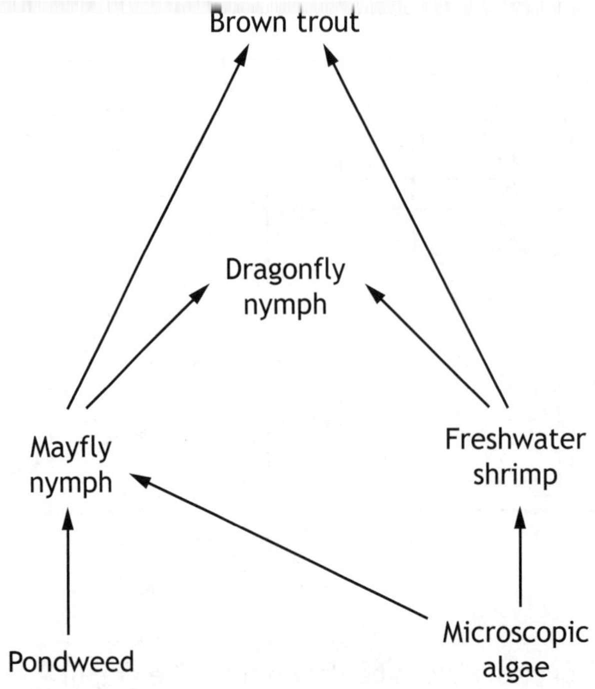

The number of freshwater shrimps was found to have decreased dramatically.

Predict the effect this will have on the numbers of dragonfly nymphs and microscopic algae.

A Both populations would decrease.

B Both populations would increase.

C Microscopic algae would decrease and dragonfly nymphs would increase.

D Microscopic algae would increase and dragonfly nymphs would decrease.

[END OF SECTION 1. NOW ATTEMPT THE QUESTIONS IN SECTION 2 OF YOUR QUESTION AND ANSWER BOOKLET]

FOR OFFICIAL USE

N5

National Qualifications 2016

Mark

X707/75/01

Biology
Section 1—Answer Grid and Section 2

MONDAY, 9 MAY

1:00 PM – 3:00 PM

Fill in these boxes and read what is printed below.

Full name of centre

Town

Forename(s)

Surname

Number of seat

Date of birth

Day Month Year

Scottish candidate number

Total marks — 80

SECTION 1 — 20 marks

Attempt ALL questions.

Instructions for the completion of Section 1 are given on *Page two*.

SECTION 2 — 60 marks

Attempt ALL questions.

Write your answers clearly in the spaces provided in this booklet. Additional space for answers and rough work is provided at the end of this booklet. If you use this space you must clearly identify the question number you are attempting. Any rough work must be written in this booklet. You should score through your rough work when you have written your final copy.

Use **blue** or **black** ink.

Before leaving the examination room you must give this booklet to the Invigilator; if you do not, you may lose all the marks for this paper.

SQA

SECTION 1 — 20 marks

The questions for Section 1 are contained in the question paper X707/75/02.

Read these and record your answers on the answer grid on *Page three* opposite.

Use **blue** or **black** ink. Do NOT use gel pens or pencil.

1. The answer to each question is **either** A, B, C or D. Decide what your answer is, then fill in the appropriate bubble (see sample question below).

2. There is **only one correct** answer to each question.

3. Any rough working should be done on the additional space for answers and rough work at the end of this booklet.

Sample Question

The thigh bone is called the

A humerus

B femur

C tibia

D fibula.

The correct answer is **B** — femur. The answer **B** bubble has been clearly filled in (see below).

A B C D

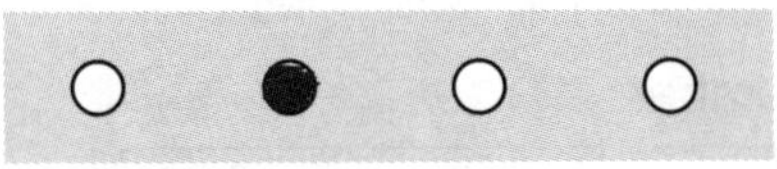

Changing an answer

If you decide to change your answer, cancel your first answer by putting a cross through it (see below) and fill in the answer you want. The answer below has been changed to **D**.

A B C D

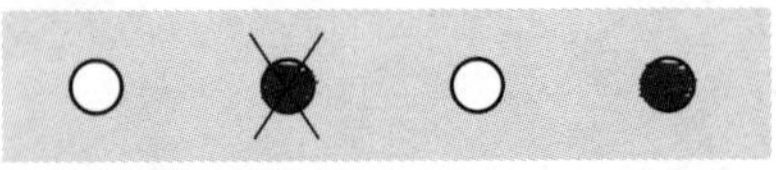

If you then decide to change back to an answer you have already scored out, put a tick (✓) to the **right** of the answer you want, as shown below:

A B C D

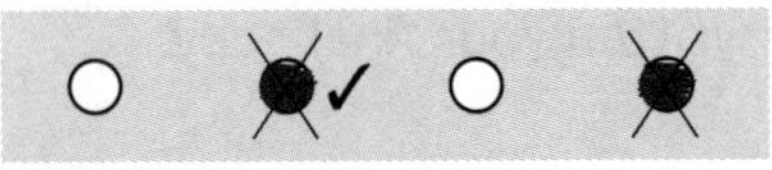

or

A B C D

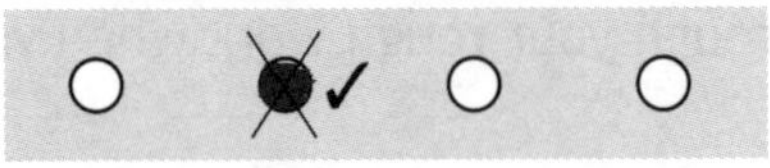

SECTION 1 — Answer Grid

	A	B	C	D
1	○	○	○	○
2	○	○	○	○
3	○	○	○	○
4	○	○	○	○
5	○	○	○	○
6	○	○	○	○
7	○	○	○	○
8	○	○	○	○
9	○	○	○	○
10	○	○	○	○
11	○	○	○	○
12	○	○	○	○
13	○	○	○	○
14	○	○	○	○
15	○	○	○	○
16	○	○	○	○
17	○	○	○	○
18	○	○	○	○
19	○	○	○	○
20	○	○	○	○

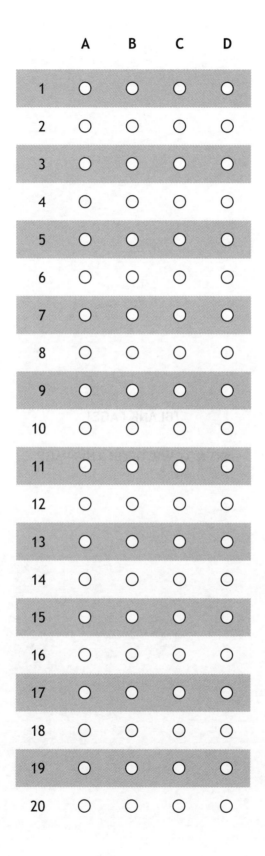

[BLANK PAGE]

DO NOT WRITE ON THIS PAGE

MARKS DO NOT WRITE IN THIS MARGIN

SECTION 2 — 60 marks

Attempt ALL questions

1. (a) State a feature of the cell membrane which allows the movement of only some substances into the cell. 1

____

(b) Osmosis is a process which can occur across the cell membrane.

(i) Choose either the leaf cell or red blood cell by ticking (✓) one of the boxes below.

Describe the effect of osmosis on this type of cell if it was placed in pure water. 1

Leaf cell ☐ Red blood cell ☐

Effect on the cell ______________________________

____

(ii) 1 Name a process, other than osmosis, which allows molecules to pass through the cell membrane. 1

____

2 Give a definition of the process chosen. 1

____

____

____

[Turn over

MARKS DO NOT WRITE IN THIS MARGIN

2. The diagram below shows how the enzyme lactase is used in the production of lactose-free milk.

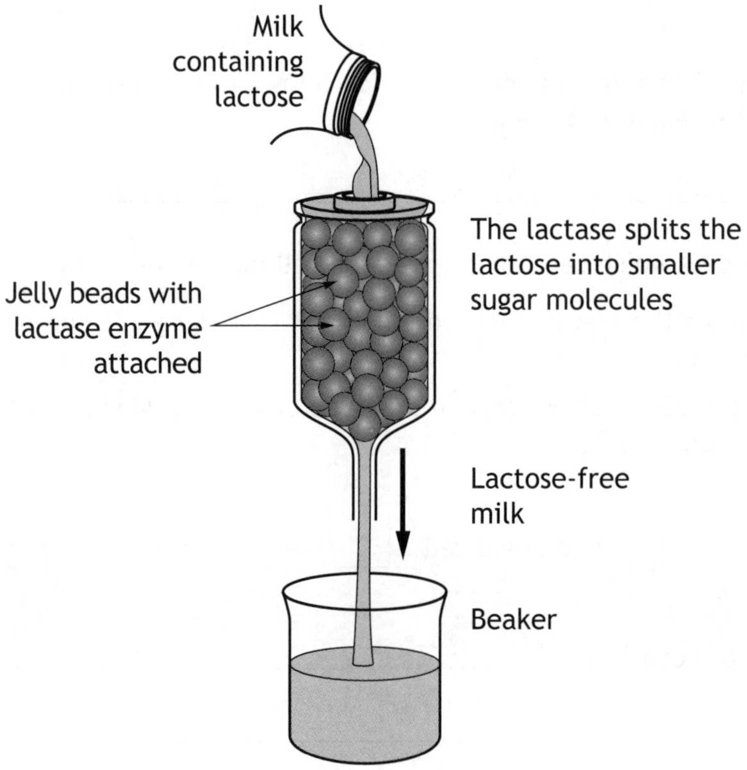

(a) (i) Underline **one** option in each of the brackets to make the following sentences correct. **2**

This process is an example of a {degradation / synthesis} reaction.

In this reaction, lactose is the {product / substrate} of lactase.

MARKS DO NOT WRITE IN THIS MARGIN

2. (a) (continued)

(ii) A fault in the production resulted in boiling water running over the lactase enzyme.

Using your knowledge of enzymes, predict how the milk produced would differ from the expected product.

Explain your answer. **2**

Prediction ______________________________

____

Explanation ______________________________

____

(b) Enzymes such as lactase are biological catalysts.

Explain the role of enzymes in living cells. **1**

____

____

(c) Name the substance of which enzymes are made. **1**

____

[Turn over

MARKS | DO NOT WRITE IN THIS MARGIN

3. The diagram below represents part of the process of genetic engineering.

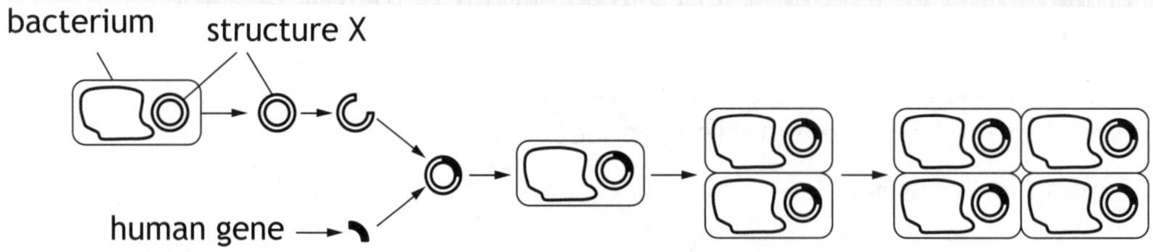

(a) (i) Structure X is removed from the bacterium and modified during this process.

Name structure X. **1**

____

(ii) The bacteria have an initial concentration of 1000 cells/cm^3.

Each cell divides once every 30 minutes.

Calculate how long it will take for the concentration to become greater than 15 000 cells/cm^3. **1**

Space for calculation

____________ hours

(b) The genetically modified bacteria are grown in a fermenter.

(i) Explain why the fermenter must be sterilised using aseptic techniques before it is used. **1**

____

____

(ii) The fermenter is controlled to provide optimum conditions.

Name one factor which can be controlled. **1**

____

MARKS DO NOT WRITE IN THIS MARGIN

4. The diagram below shows muscle cells.

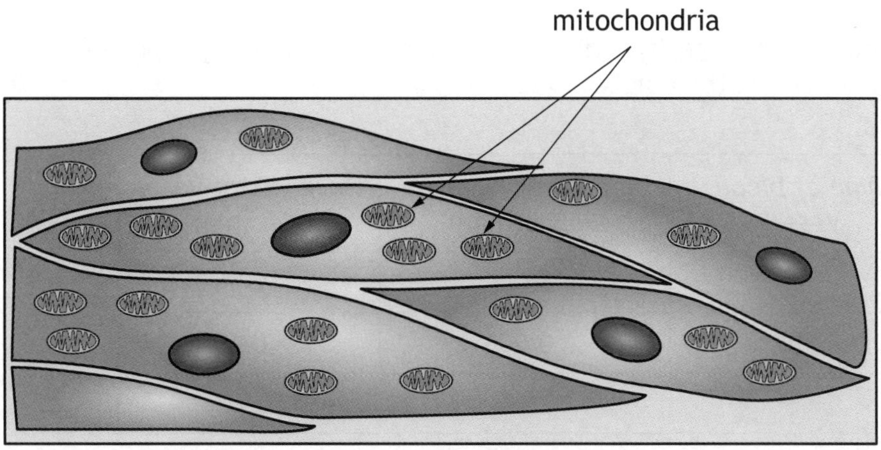

(a) (i) Explain why muscle cells require many mitochondria. 1

____

____

(ii) Name **one** substance produced by a cell carrying out aerobic respiration. 1

____

(b) A muscle cell will carry out fermentation when oxygen is not available.

Describe the fermentation pathway in muscle cells. 3

____

____

____

____

____

____

____

____

____

MARKS DO NOT WRITE IN THIS MARGIN

5. The table below gives information about features of three different types of blood vessel.

(a) (i) Complete the table by writing the name of the missing types of blood vessels in the empty boxes. 2

Type of blood vessel	*Diameter of central channel* (mm)	*Thickness of vessel wall* (mm)
	30·0	1·5
Capillary	0·006	0·001
	25·0	2·0

(ii) Of all the blood vessels, capillaries are best adapted for gas exchange.

Using the information in the table, give a reason for this. 1

(b) The heart is a muscle which pumps blood around the body and requires its own blood supply.

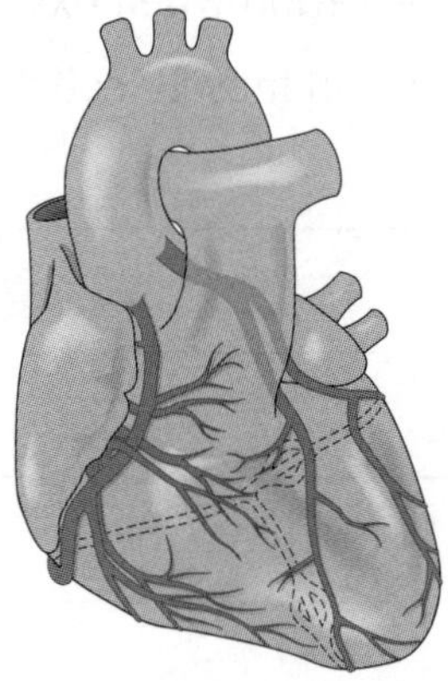

Name the blood vessel which supplies the heart muscle with blood. 1

MARKS | DO NOT WRITE IN THIS MARGIN

6. The following diagram represents part of a family tree showing the inheritance of hitchhiker's thumb, where the thumb can bend back as shown below.

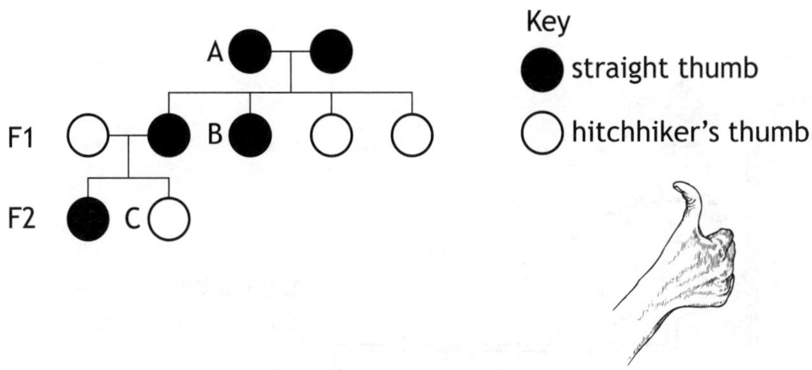

(a) Complete the table below for individuals A and C. **2**

Individual	*Possible Genotype(s)*	*Phenotype*
A		straight thumb
B	TT or Tt	straight thumb
C	tt	

(b) In a survey of 90 students it was found that 25 of them had hitchhiker's thumb.

(i) Calculate the number of students with straight thumb to hitchhiker's thumb as a simple, whole number ratio. **1**

Space for calculation

__________ : __________

straight thumb   hitchhiker's thumb

(ii) The predicted ratio was 3 straight thumb : 1 hitchhiker's thumb.

Explain why the predicted ratio was different to the actual ratio. **1**

____

____

MARKS DO NOT WRITE IN THIS MARGIN

7. (a) The rate of transpiration in plants can be measured using the apparatus shown below.

As the plant transpires, coloured water is drawn up the glass tube and its volume measured, over a set period of time, to give the rate of transpiration.

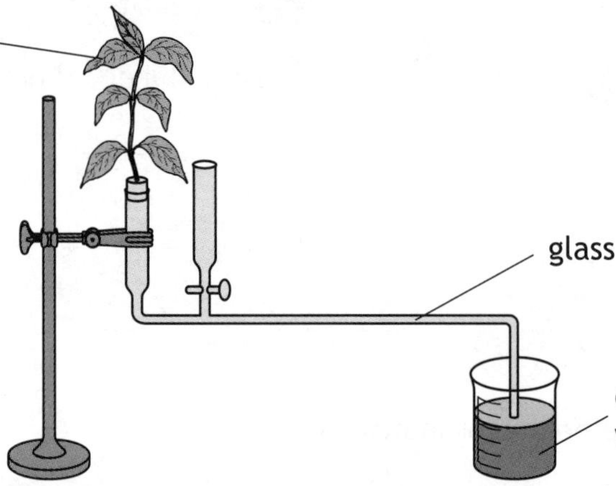

Changes in the surrounding environment can have an effect on the rate of transpiration.

(i) Select **one** of the environmental changes listed below by circling it.

increase in humidity	increase in temperature	increase in wind speed

State the effect of this change on the rate of transpiration. 1

____

(ii) Choose any of the environmental changes listed above and describe an addition to the apparatus shown, which would allow an investigation into its effect. 1

Environmental change ______________________________

Description of addition ______________________________

____

____

____

MARKS DO NOT WRITE IN THIS MARGIN

7. (continued)

(b) The graph below shows transpiration rates of two plants, P and Q.

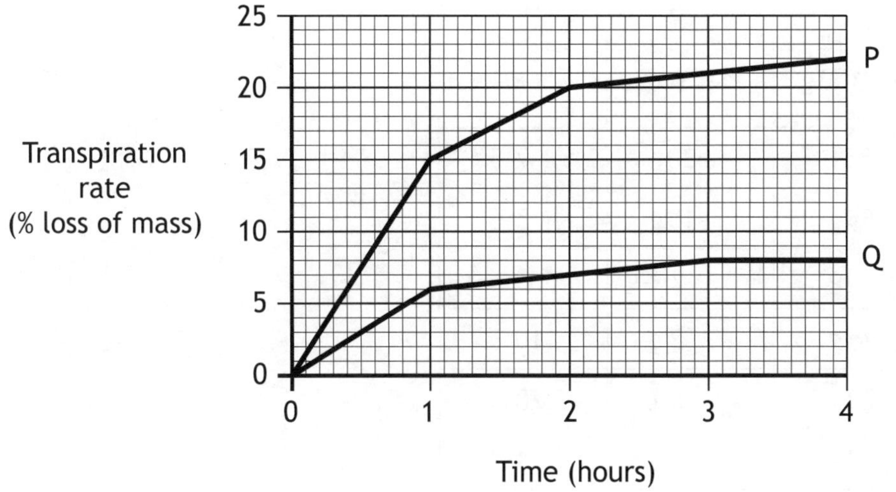

(i) With reference to the number of stomata, suggest a reason for the different transpiration rates of plants P and Q. **1**

(ii) Name the type of cells which control the opening and closing of stomata. **1**

[Turn over

MARKS DO NOT WRITE IN THIS MARGIN

8. Nutritional information helps people make an informed choice about the food they eat.

Table 1 – Label from a bar of chocolate

Nutritional information	*per* 100 g	*per bar*	% *RI**
Energy (kJ)	2251	630	7·5
Sugar	65 g	18 g	15·6
Protein	10 g	2·8 g	3
Total fat	25 g	7 g	10
Saturated fat	20 g	5·6 g	28
Salt	0·4g	0·1 g	1·7

*RI = Reference Intake (formerly "guideline daily amount")

Table 2 – Guidelines on salt content

Salt category	*Salt content* (g/100 g)
High	More than 1·5
Medium	0·3 to 1·5
Low	Less than 0·3

(a) Using information from **Table 1 and Table 2**, identify the salt category to which this chocolate bar belongs. 1

____

MARKS | DO NOT WRITE IN THIS MARGIN

8. (continued)

(b) Use the information in **Table 1** to complete the pie chart below to show the composition of protein, sugar and total fat in 100 g of the chocolate. **2**

(An additional pie chart, if required, can be found on *Page twenty-six*)

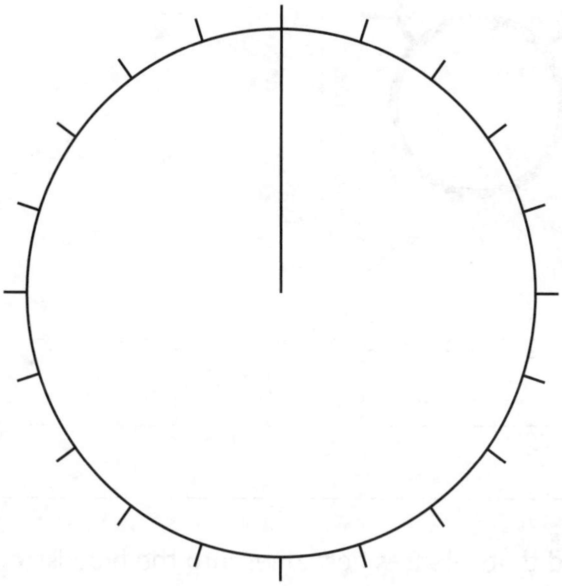

(c) (i) As shown in Table 1, saturated fat makes up part of the total fat in this chocolate bar.

Calculate the percentage of total fat which is saturated. **1**

Space for calculation

______________ %

(ii) One bar of this chocolate contains 630 kilojoules which is 7·5% of the reference intake (RI).

Calculate the total number of kilojoules which should be consumed daily. **1**

Space for calculation

______________ kilojoules

MARKS | DO NOT WRITE IN THIS MARGIN

9. (a) The diagram below represents a hormone binding to a cell within its target tissue.

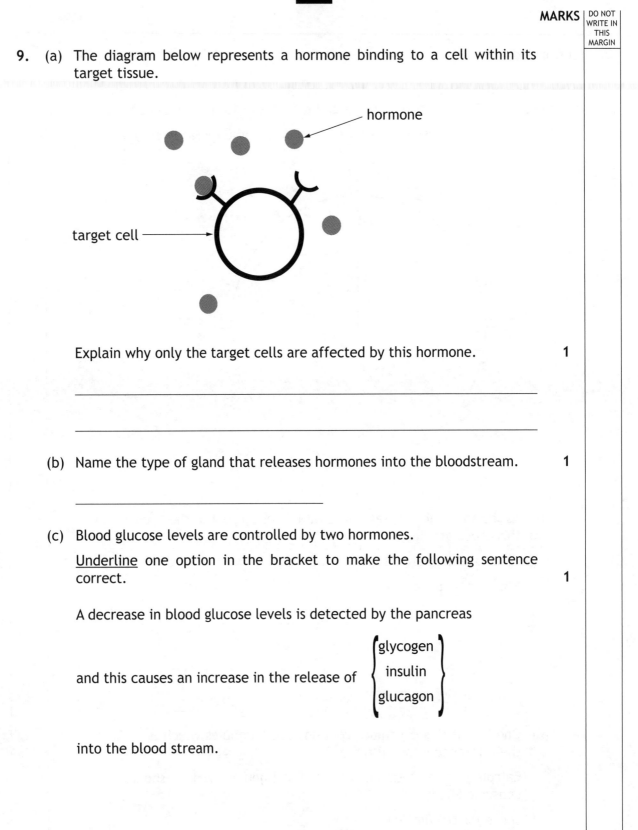

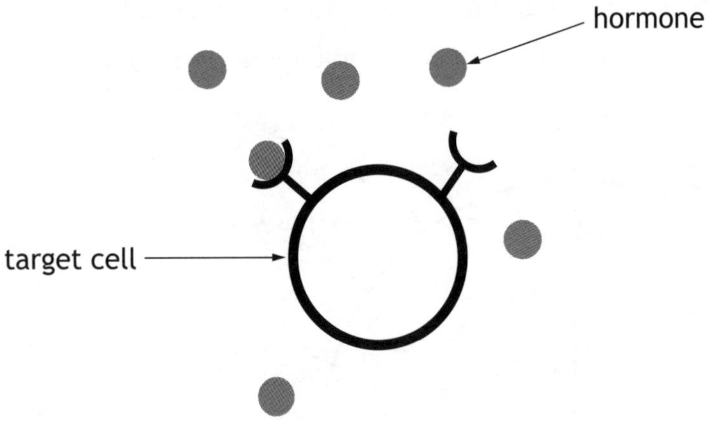

Explain why only the target cells are affected by this hormone. **1**

____

____

(b) Name the type of gland that releases hormones into the bloodstream. **1**

____

(c) Blood glucose levels are controlled by two hormones.

Underline one option in the bracket to make the following sentence correct. **1**

A decrease in blood glucose levels is detected by the pancreas

and this causes an increase in the release of {glycogen / insulin / glucagon}

into the blood stream.

MARKS | DO NOT WRITE IN THIS MARGIN

10. A food chain from a river is shown below.

algae ⟶ water flea ⟶ stickleback ⟶ perch

Using the information in the food chain, answer the following questions.

(a) (i) Identify an organism which is **both** predator and prey. **1**

____

(ii) Pesticides are known to run off from the land into rivers and enter the food chains.

Name the organism which would accumulate the greatest concentration of pesticides in its body over a period of time. **1**

____

(b) State **one** way in which energy may be lost between stages in a food chain. **1**

____

[Turn over

MARKS DO NOT WRITE IN THIS MARGIN

11. (a) In an investigation, students estimated the population and biomass of some organisms found on part of a rocky shore.

The table below shows the results.

Organism	*Population*	*Average mass of one organism* (g)	*Biomass of population* (g)
Seaweed	220	500	110 000
Limpet	1 100		33 000
Crab	100	90	9 000
Gull	5	700	3 500

(i) Complete the table to show the average mass of one limpet. **1**

Space for calculation

(ii) The total mass of living material decreases at each level in the food chain. This can be shown as a pyramid of biomass.

Complete the diagram below by entering the names of the organisms from the table into the appropriate section. **1**

(An additional diagram, if required, can be found on *Page twenty-six*)

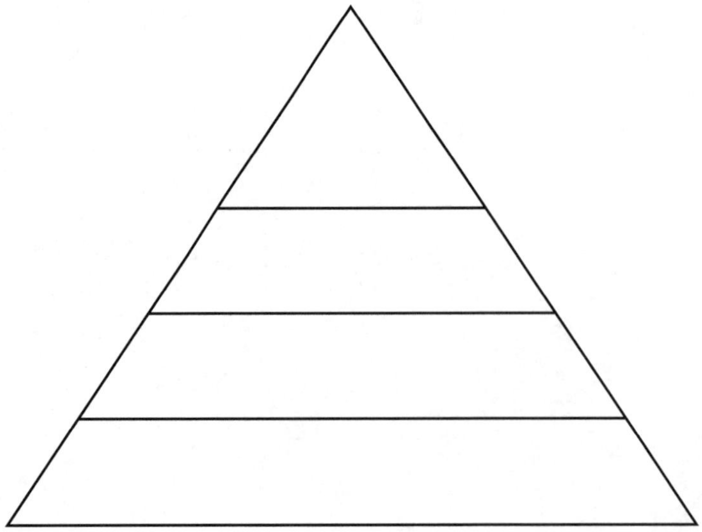

MARKS DO NOT WRITE IN THIS MARGIN

11. (continued)

(b) During the investigation the students found four different species of periwinkles at different positions on the rocky shore.

The highest position that the sea water reaches on the shore is called the high tide level.

The bars in the table below represent the positions on the shore where each species of periwinkle was found.

	Species of periwinkle			
Position on shore	*Small*	*Edible*	*Rough*	*Flat*
High tide level ↓ Low tide level				

(i) State which species of periwinkle is least likely to compete with the small periwinkle.

Explain your answer. **1**

Species ______________________________

Explanation ______________________________

____

(ii) Using the information given, explain why the competition between these periwinkles is described as interspecific. **1**

____

____

MARKS | DO NOT WRITE IN THIS MARGIN

12. A group of students carried out a five year investigation into plant growth in an area of abandoned farmland.

They sampled the area using quadrats.

The results are shown in the table below.

	Average abundance of each plant		
Year	*Meadow grass*	*Ragwort*	*Pink campion*
2011	8	15	9
2012	16	14	7
2013	24	12	4
2014	25	8	2
2015	25	5	1

(a) (i) Calculate the average decrease per year in the abundance of ragwort over the five-year period. **1**

Space for calculation

____

(ii) **Use information from the table** to suggest why the ragwort abundance decreased over the five-year period. **1**

____

____

____

(b) The students also sampled invertebrates such as beetles and spiders.

Name a sampling technique they could have used and describe a possible source of error with this technique. **2**

Sampling technique ______________

Source of error ______________

____

MARKS DO NOT WRITE IN THIS MARGIN

12. (continued)

(c) The following table gives information about some of the flowering plants found in the area.

Plant	*Height range* (cm)	*Flower colour*	*Flowering period* (months)
Pink campion	30-90	pink	6
Ragwort	30-200	yellow	6
Meadow grass	30-70	green	3
Buttercup	5-90	yellow	5

Using the information in the table, complete the three boxes in the paired statement key below. **3**

1. Flower colour is yellow — go to 2

   Flower colour is not yellow — [ ]

2. Height of plant can be over 100 cm — Ragwort

   Height of plant is under 100 cm — [ ]

3. Flowering period lasts only 3 months — Meadow Grass

   Flowering period is longer than 3 months — [ ]

[Turn over

MARKS DO NOT WRITE IN THIS MARGIN

13. The diagrams below show the light and dark varieties of a moth which can be found in woodland areas. These moths rest on the bark of trees during the day and can be eaten by birds. Normally the bark of trees in the woodland is light coloured. However in industrial areas, pollutants cause the tree bark to darken.

Woodland area

Industrial area

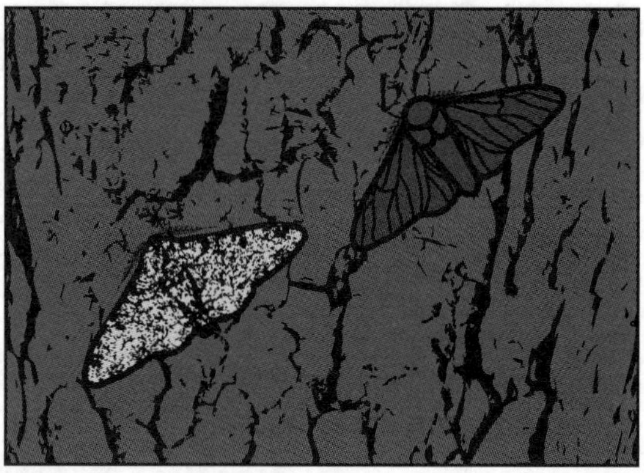

(a) The dark variety of the moth is the result of a random change in the genetic information.

State the term used to describe this change. **1**

(b) An investigation into the population of these moths in a woodland was carried out. The moths were captured, marked and released. 24 hours later the moths were recaptured.

The results are shown in the following table.

Variety of moth	*Number of moths marked and released*	*Number of marked moths recaptured*	*Marked moths recaptured (%)*
Light	480	264	55
Dark	520	208	40

(i) Suggest a reason why the number of the marked moths recaptured was worked out as a percentage. **1**

MARKS DO NOT WRITE IN THIS MARGIN

13. (b) (continued)

(ii) The woodland was in a non-industrial area.

Explain why the percentage of light moths recaptured was higher than dark moths. 1

(iii) Name the process which results in the better adapted variety of moth being more likely to survive and reproduce. 1

[Turn over

MARKS DO NOT WRITE IN THIS MARGIN

14. Red spider mites are a common pest which destroy tomato plants. Some of the mites are resistant to chemical pesticides.

Tomato growers aimed to investigate whether a predator would reduce the spider mite numbers in their greenhouses. Two identical greenhouses were used and the predator was released into only one greenhouse.

The results are shown in the graph below.

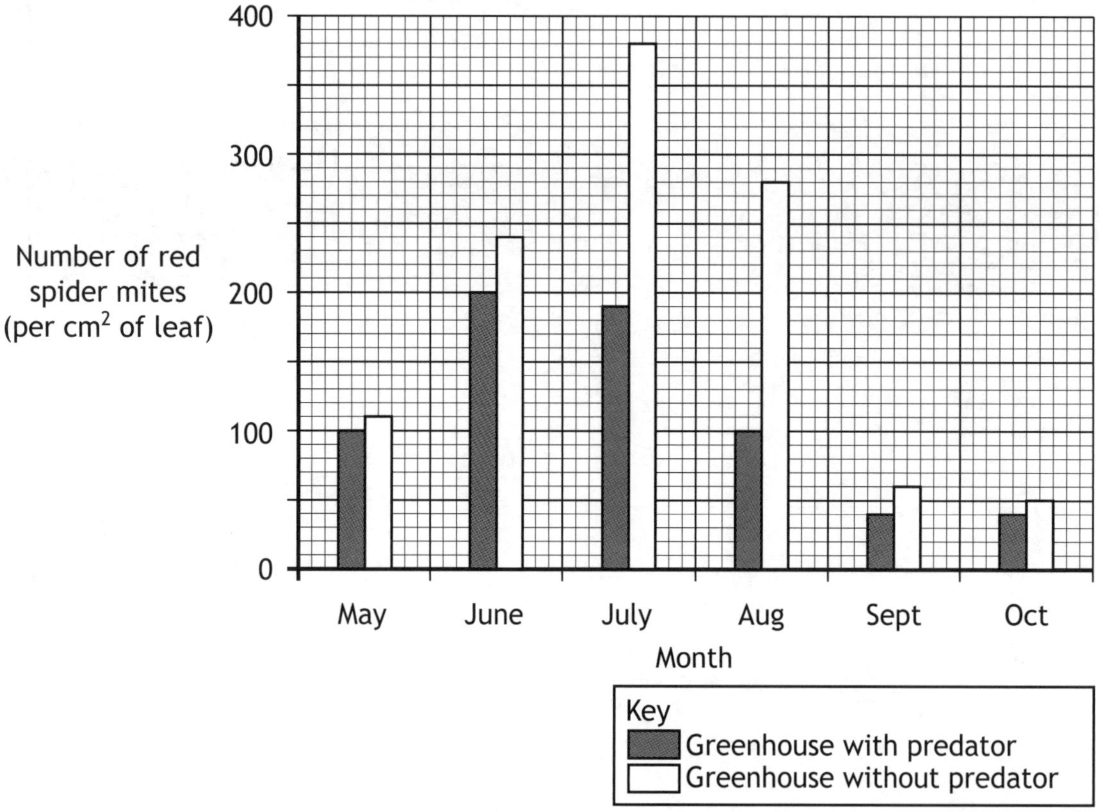

(a) (i) With reference to the aim of this investigation, give the conclusion that the tomato growers would have drawn from these results. **1**

____

____

MARKS DO NOT WRITE IN THIS MARGIN

14. (a) (continued)

(ii) The greenhouse containing tomato plants without predators was included as a control experiment.

State the purpose of the control in this investigation. 1

(b) State the term which describes the use of a predator as an alternative to pesticides. 1

[END OF QUESTION PAPER]

MARKS | DO NOT WRITE IN THIS MARGIN

ADDITIONAL SPACE FOR ANSWERS AND ROUGH WORK

ADDITIONAL PIE CHART FOR QUESTION 8(b)

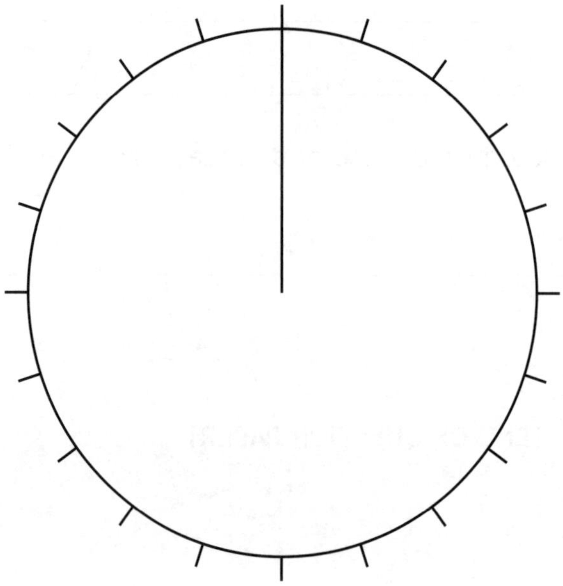

ADDITIONAL DIAGRAM FOR QUESTION 11(a) (ii)

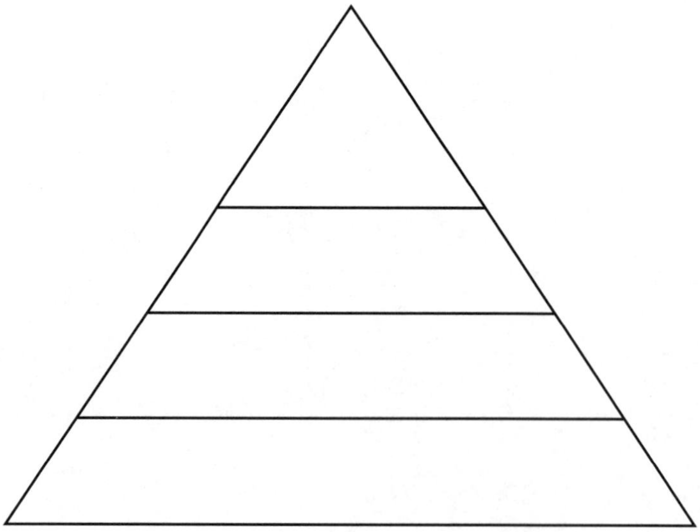

MARKS DO NOT WRITE IN THIS MARGIN

ADDITIONAL SPACE FOR ANSWERS AND ROUGH WORK

MARKS DO NOT WRITE IN THIS MARGIN

ADDITIONAL SPACE FOR ANSWERS AND ROUGH WORK

NATIONAL 5

2017

HODDER
GIBSON
LEARN MORE

N5 National Qualifications 2017

X707/75/02

Biology
Section 1—Questions

TUESDAY, 23 MAY

1:00 PM – 3:00 PM

Instructions for the completion of Section 1 are given on *Page two* of your question and answer booklet X707/75/01.

Record your answers on the answer grid on *Page three* of your question and answer booklet.

Before leaving the examination room you must give your question and answer booklet to the Invigilator; if you do not, you may lose all the marks for this paper.

SQA

SECTION 1

1. The following diagrams represent three different cells.

P

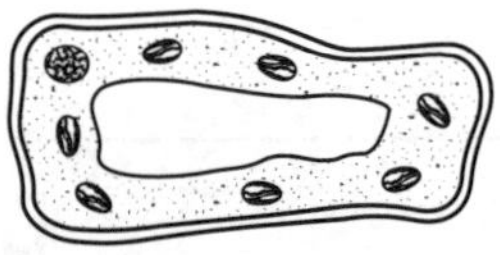

Q

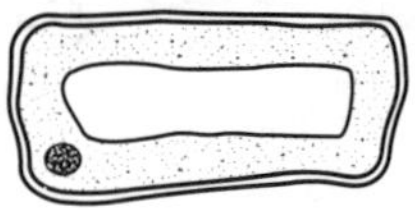

R

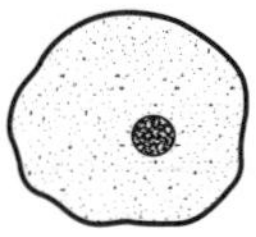

Identify the plant cell(s).

A P and R only

B P and Q only

C P only

D R only

2. The graph shows the concentrations of ions in a single-celled organism and the sea water surrounding it.

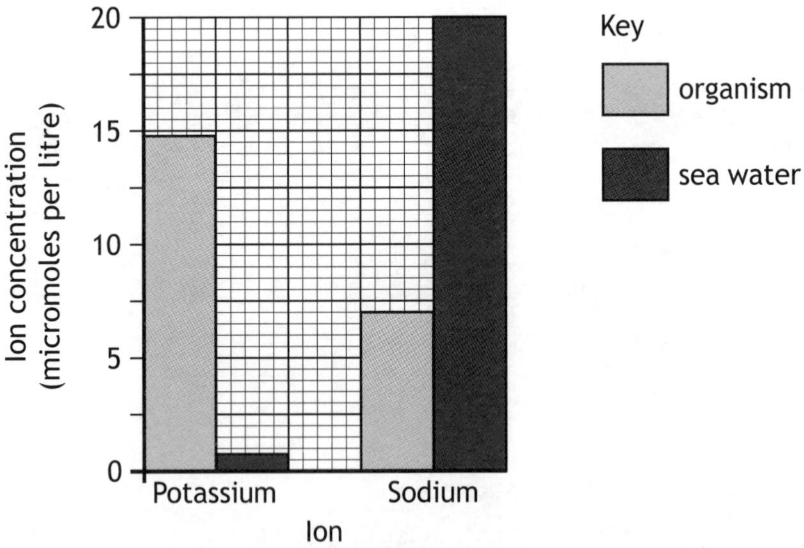

Use the graph to identify which of the following statements is correct.

A Sodium ions will move into the organism by active transport.

B Sodium ions will move out of the organism by diffusion.

C Potassium ions will move out of the organism by active transport.

D Potassium ions will move into the organism by active transport.

3. Which row in the table identifies the order of stages involved in genetic engineering?

	Stage in Genetic Engineering			
	1st	2nd	3rd	4th
A	Required gene identified	Gene and plasmid extracted	Gene inserted into plasmid	Modified cells grown
B	Required gene identified	Gene inserted into plasmid	Gene and plasmid extracted	Modified cells grown
C	Gene inserted into plasmid	Required gene identified	Modified cells grown	Gene and plasmid extracted
D	Gene inserted into plasmid	Modified cells grown	Gene and plasmid extracted	Required gene identified

4. The graph shows the effect of increasing carbon dioxide concentration on the rate of photosynthesis.

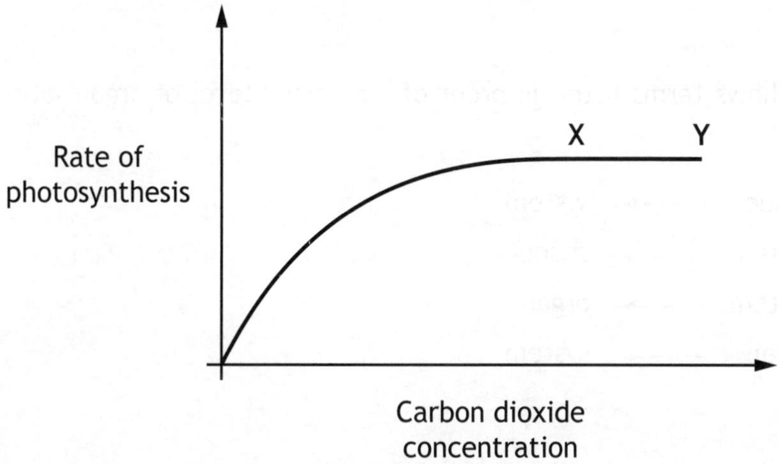

Two factors which could be limiting the rate of photosynthesis between points **X** and **Y** on the graph are

A starch concentration and light intensity

B temperature and light intensity

C temperature and carbon dioxide concentration

D sugar concentration and carbon dioxide concentration.

[Turn over

5. Which row in the table describes a process in plants which requires sugar and a substance into which sugar is converted?

	Process	*Substance*
A	Photosynthesis	Cellulose
B	Respiration	Starch
C	Photosynthesis	Protein
D	Respiration	ATP

6. What is the difference in the number of ATP molecules produced per glucose molecule by fermentation compared to aerobic respiration?

A 2

B 36

C 38

D 40

7. Which of the following shows terms listed in order of increasing level of organisation in a multicellular organism?

A organ → tissue → system

B organ → system → tissue

C tissue → system → organ

D tissue → organ → system

8. Stem cells are

A specialised cells which can divide to produce new stem cells

B specialised cells which are unable to divide to produce new stem cells

C non-specialised cells which can divide to produce new stem cells

D non-specialised cells which are unable to divide to produce new stem cells.

9. The diagram shows the main parts of a flower.

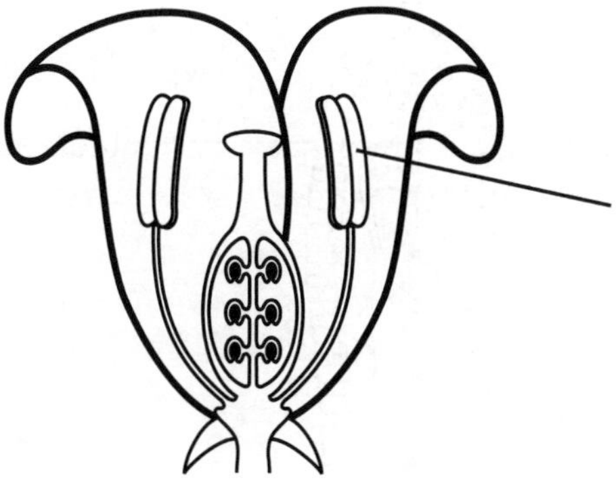

Which row in the table describes the type of gametes produced by the anther and the chromosome complement these gametes contain?

	Type of gamete produced	*Chromosome complement*
A	female	diploid
B	male	diploid
C	female	haploid
D	male	haploid

10. Which of the following shows the passage of water through the tissues when it enters a plant?

A root hair ⟶ xylem ⟶ spongy mesophyll

B root hair ⟶ spongy mesophyll ⟶ xylem

C spongy mesophyll ⟶ xylem ⟶ root hair

D xylem ⟶ spongy mesophyll ⟶ root hair

[Turn over

11. The diagram shows a villus from the small intestine.

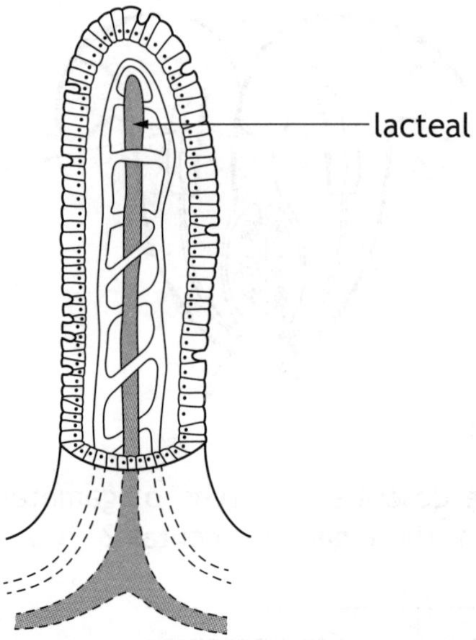

Which of the following products of digestion are both absorbed into the lacteal?

A Glycerol and fatty acids

B Glucose and fatty acids

C Glycerol and amino acids

D Glucose and amino acids

12. The process which moves food along the digestive system is called

A diffusion

B absorption

C peristalsis

D osmosis.

13. Regular physical activity can help reduce the risk of heart disease.

The table shows the percentage of males and females of different age groups, who meet the weekly recommendations for physical activity.

	Percentage meeting the weekly recommendations for physical activity	
Age group	*Males*	*Females*
16–24	83	68
25–34	75	65
35–44	74	67
45–54	69	64
55–64	61	53

Which of the following statements is **not** correct for this data?

A The percentage of males meeting the weekly recommendations always decreases as age increases.

B The percentage of females meeting the weekly recommendations always decreases as age increases.

C 26% of males aged 35–44 do not meet the weekly recommendations.

D 35% of females aged 25–34 do not meet the weekly recommendations.

14. An example of a biotic factor affecting a population of plants is

A a leaf disease reducing the growth of lettuce plants

B acidic soil preventing the growth of daisies

C shade from buildings causing a decrease in the growth of grass

D a cold winter causing a decrease in the growth of geranium plants.

[Turn over

15. Which of the following statements is true of predation?

A It is an abiotic factor and causes a decrease in prey numbers.

B It is an abiotic factor and causes an increase in prey numbers.

C It is a biotic factor and causes a decrease in prey numbers.

D It is a biotic factor and causes an increase in prey numbers.

16. On average, 90% of energy is lost at each energy transfer in a food chain.

Which of the following is a cause of this energy loss?

A Digested material

B Cell repair

C Movement

D Growth

17. The diagram below shows a pyramid of numbers.

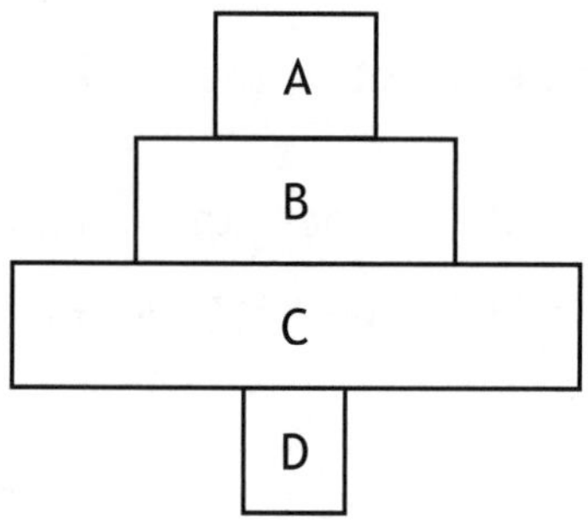

Which letter represents the producer?

18. The following graph shows the changes in wheat yield over a fifty-year period.

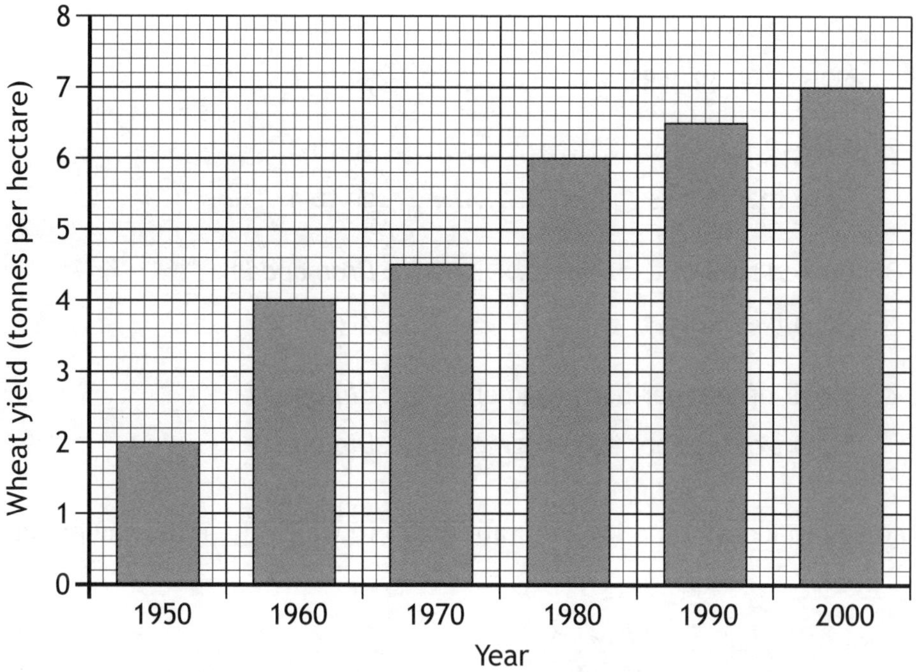

The percentage increase in wheat yield from 1950 to 2000 is

A 5

B 40

C 250

D 350.

19. Which row in the table describes a type of competition and a matching example?

	Type of competition	*Example*
A	Interspecific	Two birch trees growing close together in a wood
B	Interspecific	Lions and hyenas feeding on zebra
C	Intraspecific	Seals and dolphins feeding on small fish
D	Intraspecific	Buttercups and daisies growing in the same field

[Turn over

20. The following paired statement key can be used to identify invertebrate groups.

1. Six legs .... *Hexapoda*
   More than six legs .... go to 2
2. 8 legs .... go to 3
   More than 8 legs .... go to 4
3. Curved sting .... *Dromopoda*
   No curved sting .... *Arachnida*
4. 1 pair of legs per body segment....... *Chilopoda*
   2 pairs of legs per body segment...... *Diplopoda*

Use the key to identify the invertebrate group to which the following organism belongs.

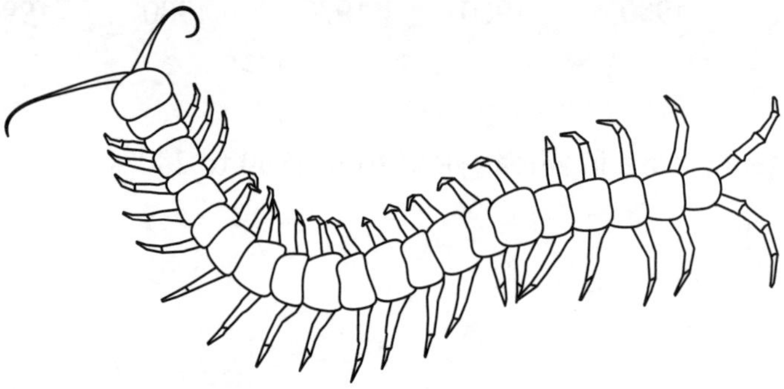

A Dromopoda

B Arachnida

C Chilopoda

D Diplopoda

[END OF SECTION 1. NOW ATTEMPT THE QUESTIONS IN SECTION 2 OF YOUR QUESTION AND ANSWER BOOKLET.]

[BLANK PAGE]

DO NOT WRITE ON THIS PAGE

[BLANK PAGE]

DO NOT WRITE ON THIS PAGE

FOR OFFICIAL USE

N5

National
Qualifications
2017

Mark

X707/75/01

Biology
Section 1—Answer Grid and Section 2

TUESDAY, 23 MAY

1:00 PM – 3:00 PM

Fill in these boxes and read what is printed below.

Full name of centre

Town

Forename(s)

Surname

Number of seat

Date of birth

Day

Month

Year

Scottish candidate number

Total marks — 80

SECTION 1 — 20 marks

Attempt ALL questions.

Instructions for the completion of Section 1 are given on *Page two*.

SECTION 2 — 60 marks

Attempt ALL questions.

Write your answers clearly in the spaces provided in this booklet. Additional space for answers and rough work is provided at the end of this booklet. If you use this space you must clearly identify the question number you are attempting. Any rough work must be written in this booklet. You should score through your rough work when you have written your final copy.

Use **blue** or **black** ink.

Before leaving the examination room you must give this booklet to the Invigilator; if you do not, you may lose all the marks for this paper.

SECTION 1— 20 marks

The questions for Section 1 are contained in the question paper X707/75/02.

Read these and record your answers on the answer grid on *Page three* opposite.

Use **blue** or **black** ink. Do NOT use gel pens or pencil.

1. The answer to each question is **either** A, B, C or D. Decide what your answer is, then fill in the appropriate bubble (see sample question below).

2. There is **only one correct** answer to each question.

3. Any rough working should be done on the additional space for answers and rough work at the end of this booklet.

Sample Question

The thigh bone is called the

A humerus

B femur

C tibia

D fibula.

The correct answer is **B** — femur. The answer **B** bubble has been clearly filled in (see below).

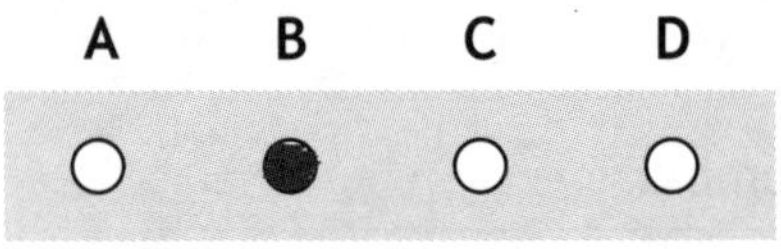

Changing an answer

If you decide to change your answer, cancel your first answer by putting a cross through it (see below) and fill in the answer you want. The answer below has been changed to **D**.

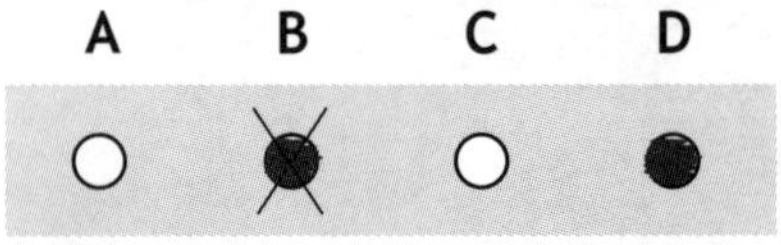

If you then decide to change back to an answer you have already scored out, put a tick (✓) to the **right** of the answer you want, as shown below:

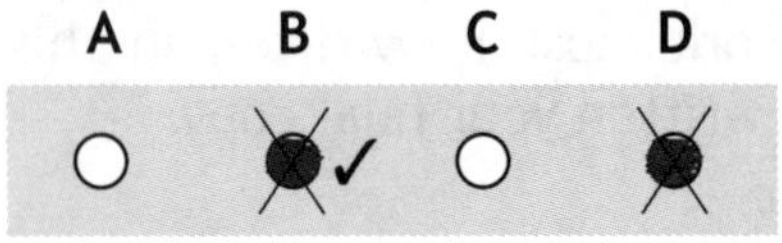

or

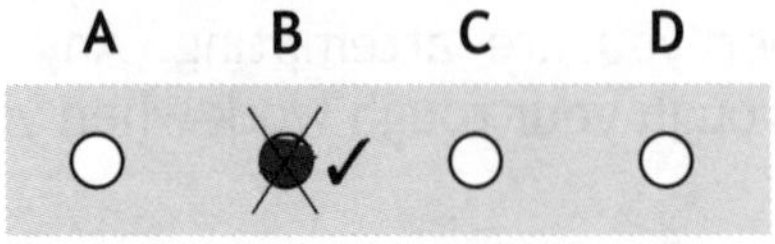

SECTION 1—Answer Grid

	A	B	C	D
1	○	○	○	○
2	○	○	○	○
3	○	○	○	○
4	○	○	○	○
5	○	○	○	○
6	○	○	○	○
7	○	○	○	○
8	○	○	○	○
9	○	○	○	○
10	○	○	○	○
11	○	○	○	○
12	○	○	○	○
13	○	○	○	○
14	○	○	○	○
15	○	○	○	○
16	○	○	○	○
17	○	○	○	○
18	○	○	○	○
19	○	○	○	○
20	○	○	○	○

[BLANK PAGE]

DO NOT WRITE ON THIS PAGE

MARKS | DO NOT WRITE IN THIS MARGIN

SECTION 2 — 60 marks

Attempt ALL questions

1. *Paramecium* is a single-celled organism which lives in fresh water.

The following diagram shows some of its structures.

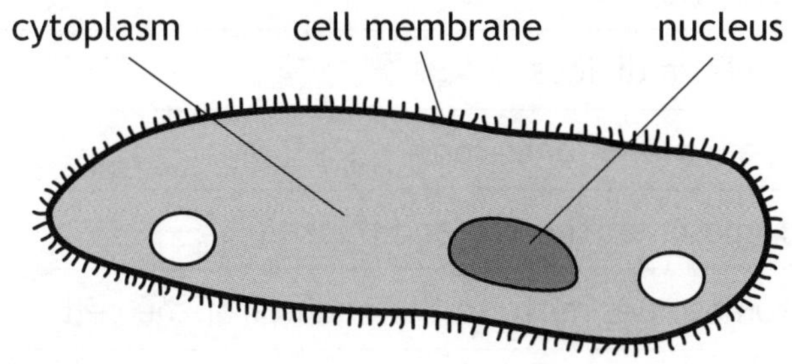

(a) (i) Choose one of the following structures by ticking (✓) one of the boxes and describe its function. **1**

Cytoplasm ☐ Cell membrane ☐ Nucleus ☐

Function ______________________________

____

(ii) The water concentration outside the paramecium is higher than the water concentration of the cytoplasm. This causes the diffusion of water into the cell.

Name this movement of water. **1**

____

(b) Name the structure present in a plant cell which prevents it from bursting when full of water. **1**

____

[Turn over

MARKS | DO NOT WRITE IN THIS MARGIN

2. (a) (i) The table describes some stages which occur during cell division, but not in the correct order.

The first stage has been given.

Identify the **third stage** by writing the number 3 beside its description. 1

Stage	*Description*
	cytoplasm divides
	nuclear membranes form
1	chromosomes shorten and thicken
	chromosomes move to the equator of the cell
	pairs of chromatids are pulled apart

(ii) The diagram represents a cell during one of the stages of mitosis.

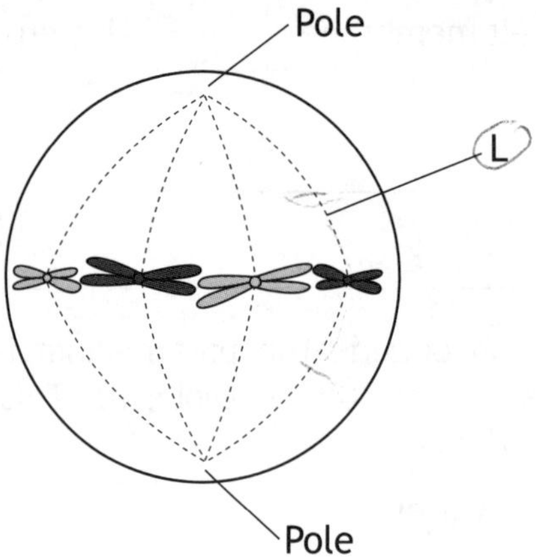

Name the part labelled L in the diagram. 1

____

(b) During mitosis a pair of chromatids was pulled apart, each moving away from the equator, towards opposite poles, at a rate of 1 micrometre per second.

Calculate the distance between them after 20 seconds. 1

Space for calculation

____________ micrometres

MARKS | DO NOT WRITE IN THIS MARGIN

3. (a) Forensic scientists can take small quantities of DNA and use a process to make large quantities. Each DNA molecule is separated and used to make two complementary strands as shown below.

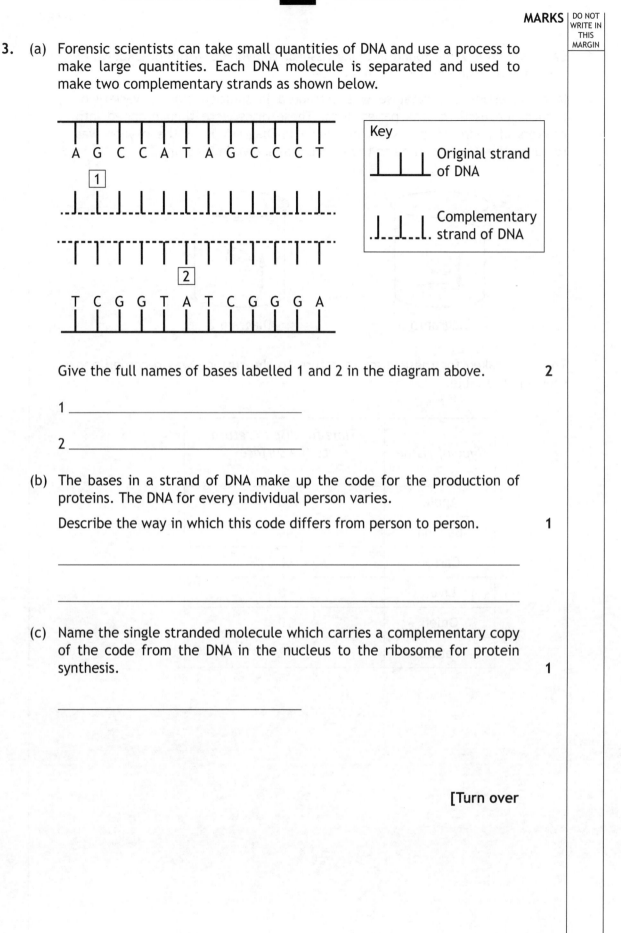

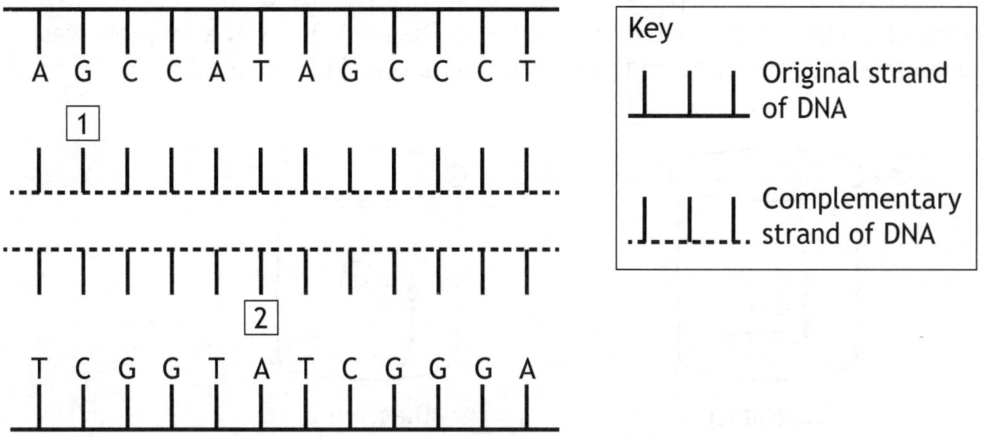

Give the full names of bases labelled 1 and 2 in the diagram above. **2**

1 ______________________________

2 ______________________________

(b) The bases in a strand of DNA make up the code for the production of proteins. The DNA for every individual person varies.

Describe the way in which this code differs from person to person. **1**

____

____

(c) Name the single stranded molecule which carries a complementary copy of the code from the DNA in the nucleus to the ribosome for protein synthesis. **1**

____

[Turn over

MARKS DO NOT WRITE IN THIS MARGIN

4. Catalase, an enzyme found in living tissues, is involved in the breakdown of hydrogen peroxide into water and oxygen.

In an investigation, catalase was extracted in solution from a variety of tissues and used to soak paper discs. These discs were then dropped into beakers of hydrogen peroxide, as shown in Diagram 1. As the oxygen was released the discs returned to the surface, as shown in Diagram 2.

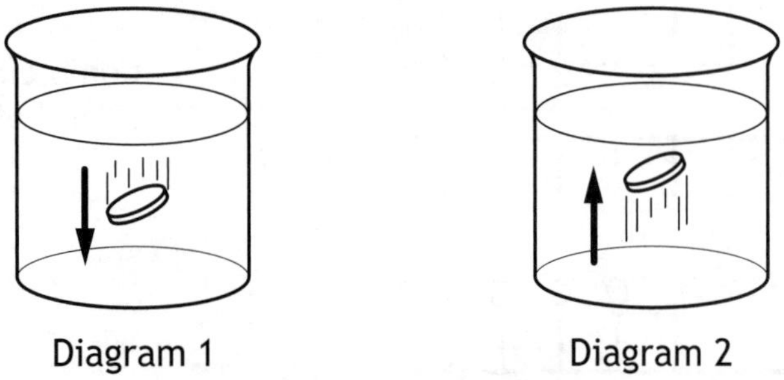

The time taken for these discs to return to the surface was recorded and shown in the table.

Type of tissue	*Time for disc to return to the surface* (s)
Apple	108
Banana	44
Carrot	68
Liver	8
Onion	70
Potato	72

MARKS DO NOT WRITE IN THIS MARGIN

4. (continued)

(a) On the grid below, complete the vertical axis and the remaining bars to show the time taken for the discs to return to the surface, for each tissue. 2

(An additional grid, if required, can be found on *Page twenty-six*)

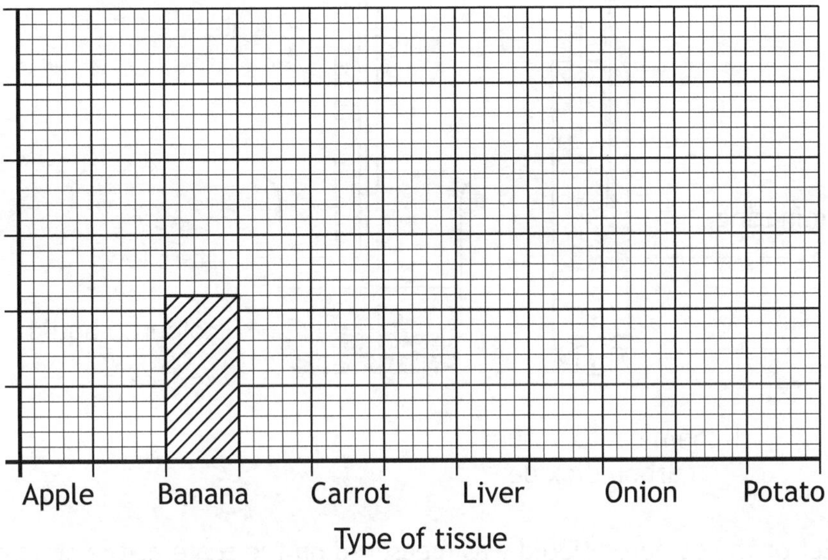

(b) The aim of the experiment was to investigate catalase activity in a variety of tissues.

Using the information given, write an appropriate conclusion for this experiment. 1

Conclusion ____________________

____

____

(c) The experiment was carried out at pH 7, the optimum pH for catalase.

Complete the following sentence, using the words **increase, decrease** or **stay the same**, to predict what would happen if the experiment was repeated at pH 4. 1

At pH 4, the rate of oxygen production would ____________________ in each tissue.

[Turn over

MARKS DO NOT WRITE IN THIS MARGIN

5. A student investigated the effect of temperature on the rate of respiration in germinating (growing) peas. Using the arrangement shown, four respirometers labelled A–D were set up at the temperatures shown in the table below.

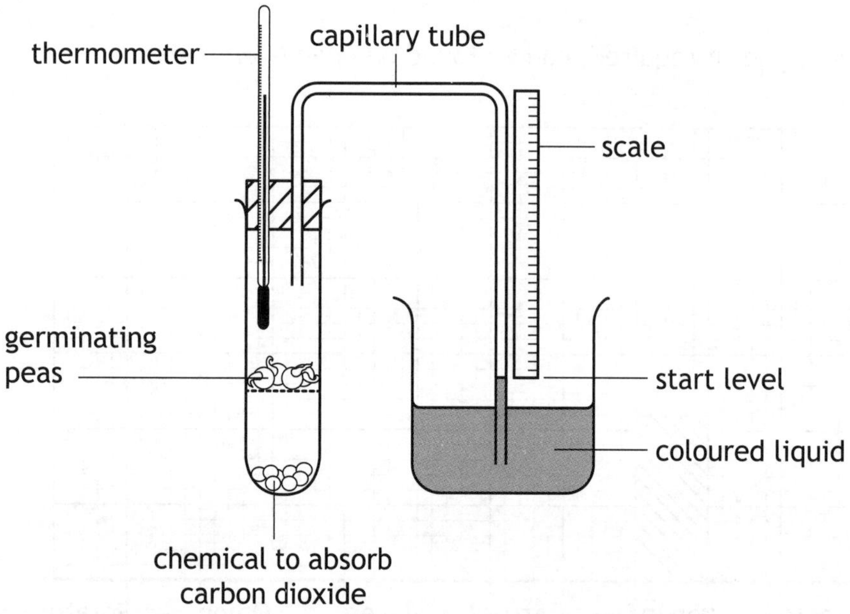

The level of the coloured liquid was measured on the scale at the start of the investigation and again after 20 minutes. The rise in liquid level was due to oxygen uptake by the germinating peas. The results are shown in the table.

Respirometer	*Temperature* (°C)	*Contents*	*Rise in liquid level* (mm)	*Rate of oxygen uptake* (mm per minute)
A	15	Germinating peas	14	0·7
B	15	Dead peas	0	0
C	25	Germinating peas	26	
D	25	Dead peas	0	0

(a) (i) Complete the table above by calculating the rate of oxygen uptake per minute by the peas in respirometer C. **1**

Space for calculation

MARKS | DO NOT WRITE IN THIS MARGIN

5. (a) (continued)

(ii) Using the results from the table complete the following conclusion by underlining one option in the bracket. **1**

Increasing the { temperature / liquid level / oxygen uptake } increases the rate of respiration in germinating peas.

(iii) Another respirometer was set up at 60 °C with germinating peas and the coloured liquid did not rise. The student concluded that the peas were not respiring.

Explain why this temperature prevented the peas from carrying out respiration. **2**

____

____

____

(iv) Respirometers B and D were set up as control experiments.

Describe the purpose of the controls in **this** investigation. **1**

____

____

____

(b) The diagram below represents the fermentation pathway in a plant cell.

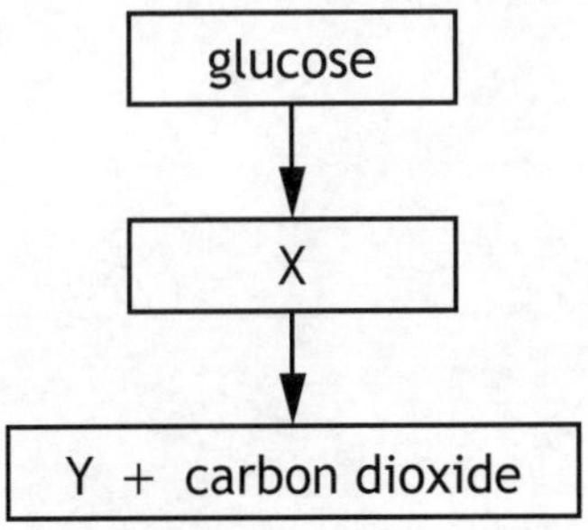

Choose either molecule X or Y and state its name. **1**

Molecule ________________

Name ________________________________

MARKS DO NOT WRITE IN THIS MARGIN

6. Chromosomes contain the genetic information responsible for variation amongst members of a species.

Fruit flies can have either a grey or black body colour.

The parent flies used in a cross are shown in the diagram.

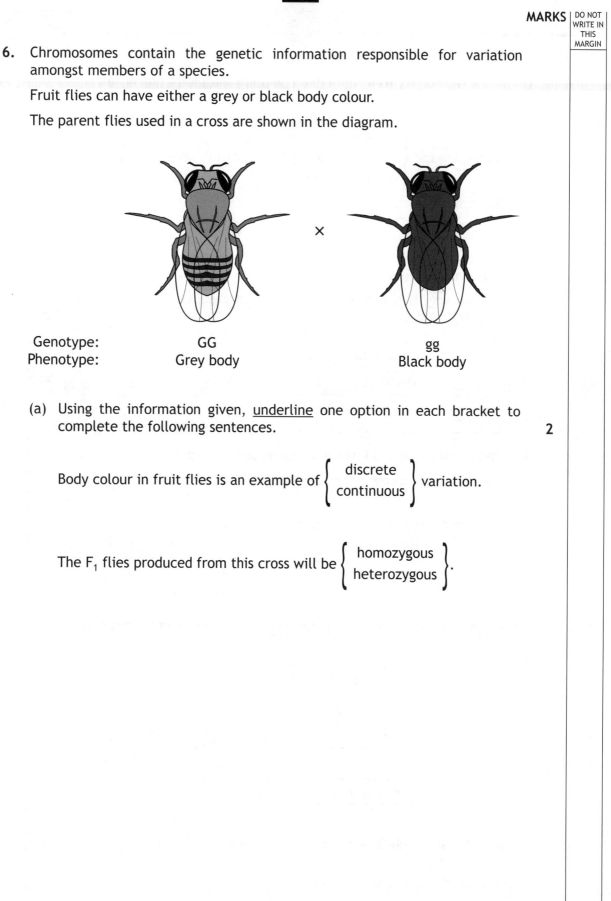

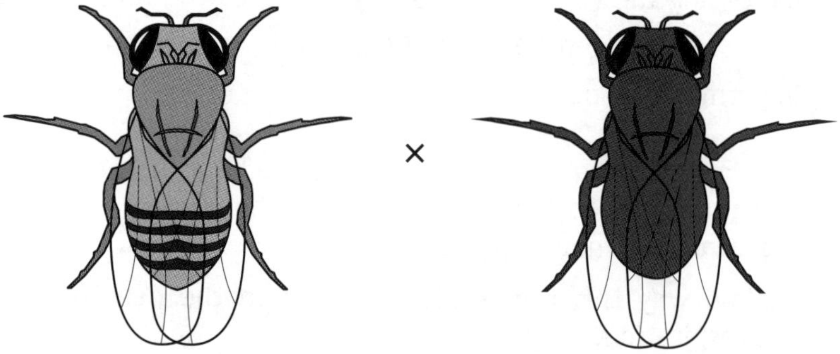

Genotype:	GG	gg
Phenotype:	Grey body	Black body

(a) Using the information given, underline one option in each bracket to complete the following sentences. **2**

Body colour in fruit flies is an example of { discrete / continuous } variation.

The F_1 flies produced from this cross will be { homozygous / heterozygous }.

MARKS DO NOT WRITE IN THIS MARGIN

6. (continued)

(b) The diagram relates to sexual reproduction in humans.

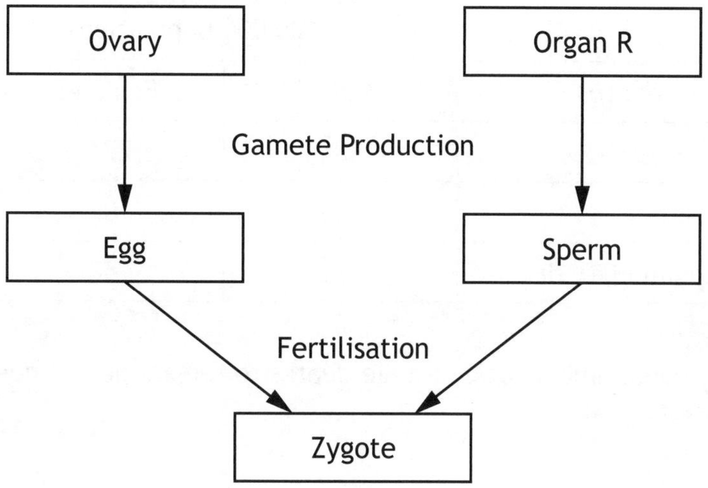

(i) Name organ R. 1

____

(ii) Describe what happens during fertilisation. 1

____

____

____

(iii) An egg cell is haploid but a zygote is diploid.

Explain what this means in terms of the chromosome complement found in each of these cells. 1

____

____

____

____

[Turn over

MARKS | DO NOT WRITE IN THIS MARGIN

7. (a) The table shows some information about causes of adult deaths in Scotland.

	Number of adult deaths (per 100 000 population)	
Cause of adult deaths	*Males*	*Females*
Cancer	385	274
Coronary heart disease	165	105
Chronic obstructive pulmonary disease	71	58

Calculate the simple whole number ratio of male deaths to female deaths due to coronary heart disease. 1

Space for calculation

________ : ________

Males *Females*

(b) (i) Coronary heart disease can gradually cause the coronary arteries to get narrower or become blocked completely.

Name **one** essential substance that will no longer be able to reach the cells in the heart if these arteries become blocked. 1

____

(ii) A person has been told that they have a high risk of developing coronary heart disease.

Suggest a lifestyle choice that they could make, other than exercising more, to help reduce this risk. 1

____

MARKS | DO NOT WRITE IN THIS MARGIN

7. (continued)

(c) Chronic obstructive pulmonary disease is a condition which affects the lungs. It can destroy the alveolar walls, leading to fewer alveoli.

The diagrams represent lung tissues which have undamaged and damaged alveoli.

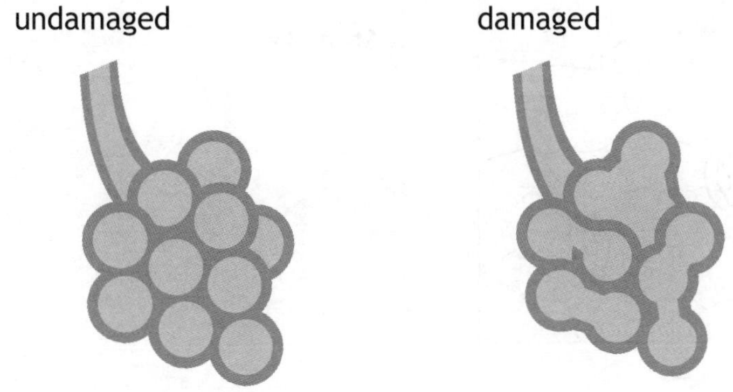

Identify a feature of the alveoli which will be affected by this reduction in their number. 1

____

[Turn over

MARKS | DO NOT WRITE IN THIS MARGIN

8. A student investigated the link between transpiration rate and the number of leaf stomata.

A microscope was used to look at the number of stomata on a leaf surface of plant species A as shown.

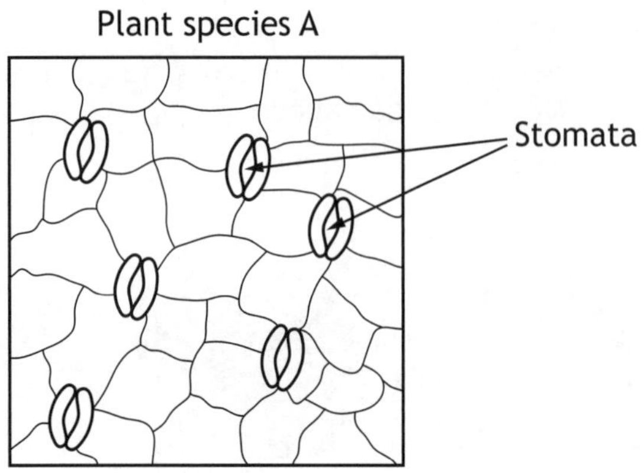

The area shown on the diagram above measures 0·04 mm^2.

(a) Calculate the expected number of stomata present in 1 mm^2 on this leaf surface. **1**

Space for calculation

____

(b) A leaf from another plant, species B, had fewer stomata per mm^2 of leaf surface and a different rate of transpiration.

It was concluded that the number of stomata present affects the rate of transpiration.

(i) Suggest an advantage to plant species B of having fewer stomata. **1**

____

____

(ii) Tick (✓) one box below to show the environmental condition to which this plant has become best adapted. **1**

Dry ☐ Cool ☐ Moist ☐

MARKS DO NOT WRITE IN THIS MARGIN

9. After a head injury, a student became dizzy and occasionally lost balance.

(a) Name the part of the brain which controls balance. 1

(b) To test if there was also damage to the spinal cord, doctors touched different areas of the student's skin with a blunt needle.

Describe how the stimulus is detected at the skin and how the message is then carried into and across the spinal cord. 4

[Turn over

MARKS | DO NOT WRITE IN THIS MARGIN

10. Type 1 diabetes occurs if the body does not produce any or enough insulin.

(a) (i) Name the organ which produces insulin. 1

(ii) As a result of Type 1 diabetes, glucose is unable to enter the cells of the body. A symptom of this is extreme tiredness.

Using your knowledge of respiration, explain why a person suffering from diabetes might show extreme tiredness. 1

(b) People with Type 1 diabetes need to inject insulin.

The table contains information about some of the different types of insulin available.

Type of insulin	*Time for insulin to start working*	*Time for insulin levels to peak*	*Duration in blood* (hours)
P	1 hour	No peak	20–26
Q	1–3 hours	8 hours	12–16
R	30–60 minutes	2–4 hours	5–8
S	15 minutes	30–90 minutes	3–5

Using information from the table, answer the following questions.

(i) A fast acting type of insulin can be injected just before meals.

Identify the type of insulin that is best suited for this. 1

(ii) Another type of insulin can be injected once a day to provide a steady supply of insulin to the body.

Identify the type of insulin that would be most effective at doing this. 1

MARKS DO NOT WRITE IN THIS MARGIN

10. (continued)

(c) Diabetes also occurs if the target tissues in the body do not respond to insulin reaching them through the bloodstream.

Name the structures found on the surface of the target tissues that respond to the hormone insulin. **1**

____

[Turn over

MARKS DO NOT WRITE IN THIS MARGIN

11. Certain varieties of potato plant are eaten by beetles, reducing the yield of potatoes. A beetle-resistant variety of potato plant was developed.

In an investigation, the beetle-resistant variety was grown outdoors in one field and the non-resistant variety grown in another.

The yields of both varieties were recorded and the results are shown in the graph below.

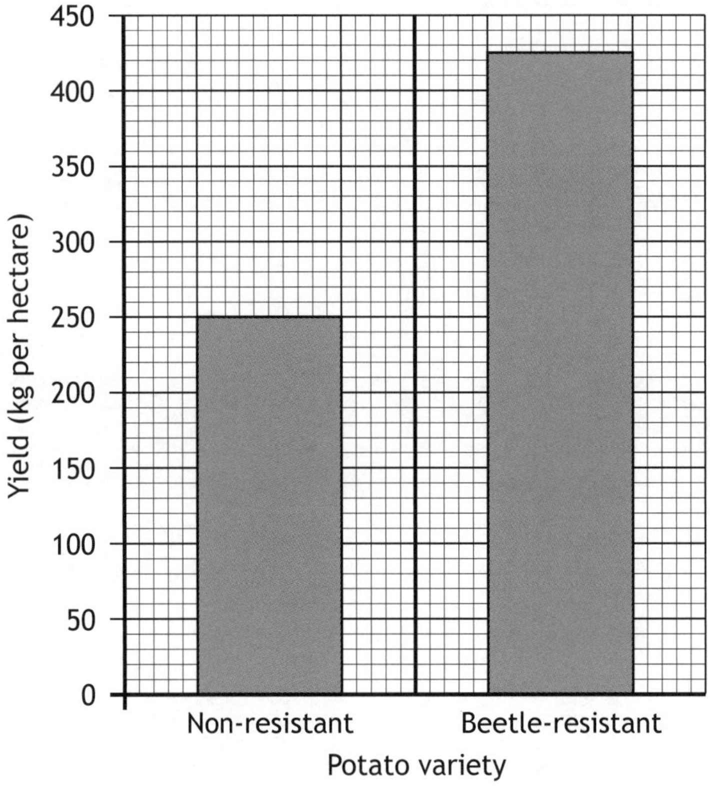

(a) Describe how the reliability of these results could be increased. **1**

____

____

(b) Calculate the difference in yield between the two varieties. **1**

Space for calculation

________________ kg per hectare

MARKS DO NOT WRITE IN THIS MARGIN

11. (continued)

(c) Identify a variable that would have to be kept the same between the two fields to ensure the results were valid. 1

____

(d) Genetic engineering was used to develop the beetle-resistant variety of potato plant.

Before the development of genetic engineering, farmers used other methods to control the beetle numbers in their potato fields.

Name **one** of these methods. 1

____

[Turn over

MARKS | DO NOT WRITE IN THIS MARGIN

12. The Scottish crossbill is a small bird which is native to Scotland. It inhabits pine forests in northern Scotland and feeds on pine seeds using its crossed beak.

(a) State the term used to describe the role of the Scottish crossbill within its community. **1**

____

(b) The shape of a crossbill's beak is a structural adaptation which is the result of a new allele being produced.

Name the process by which new alleles are produced. **1**

____

(c) The Scottish crossbill has been classified as a separate species, but can still mate with other species of crossbill.

Give a feature of any offspring produced from this mating, which proves that the parents are different species. **1**

____

MARKS | DO NOT WRITE IN THIS MARGIN

13. Decide if each of the following statements about evolution is **True** or **False** and tick (✓) the appropriate box.

If the statement is **False**, write the correct word in the **Correction** box to replace the word underlined in the statement. **3**

Statement	*True*	*False*	*Correction*
Genetic variation within a population allows the population to <u>adapt</u> in a changing environment.			
Isolation barriers can be geographical, <u>environmental</u> or reproductive.			
Sub-populations evolve until they become genetically <u>identical</u>.			

[Turn over

MARKS | DO NOT WRITE IN THIS MARGIN

14. The flow of nitrogen in a fish farm is shown in the diagram below.

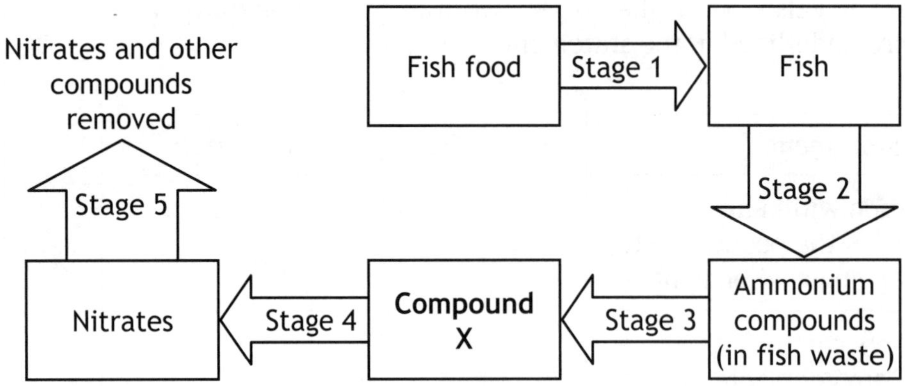

(a) (i) Name compound X. **1**

____

(ii) Give the number of a stage in the process shown above, which involves nitrifying bacteria. **1**

Stage __________

(b) In the fish farm the nitrates have to be removed from the water to prevent build-up. In some situations living organisms remove nitrates from the soil.

(i) Name the type of organism which can absorb nitrates from the soil. **1**

____

(ii) Nitrates supply organisms with nitrogen.

State why nitrogen is required. **1**

____

(c) Decomposers, such as bacteria, help to break down waste and dead organisms.

Name another type of microorganism which carries out this role. **1**

____

MARKS DO NOT WRITE IN THIS MARGIN

15. Levels of air pollution can be estimated by the presence or absence of organisms called lichens.

Air pollution level	*Most common type of lichen present*
Low	Shrubby
Medium	Leafy
High	Crusty

Environmental scientists carried out a study on lichen species at four different sites and obtained the results shown in the table below.

	Number of lichen species present		
Site	*Shrubby*	*Leafy*	*Crusty*
A	0	5	19
B	3	2	0
C	16	3	0
D	7	14	2

(a) (i) Site A had the highest levels of air pollution.

Using information from **both tables**, describe the evidence supporting this statement. 1

(ii) Calculate the average number of leafy lichen species present at the four sites. 1

Space for calculation

(b) State the name given to species, such as lichen, which are used to estimate levels of pollution. 1

[END OF QUESTION PAPER]

MARKS | DO NOT WRITE IN THIS MARGIN

ADDITIONAL SPACE FOR ANSWERS AND ROUGH WORK

ADDITIONAL GRID FOR QUESTION 4(a)

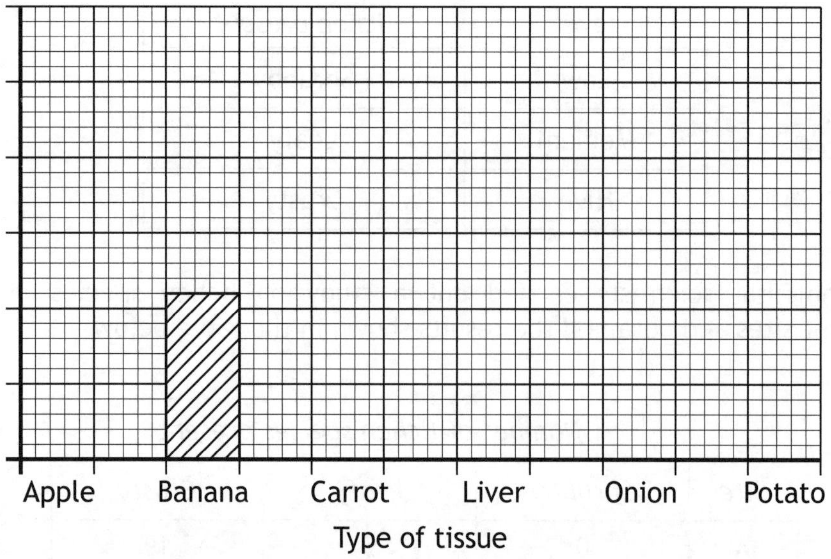

MARKS | DO NOT WRITE IN THIS MARGIN

ADDITIONAL SPACE FOR ANSWERS AND ROUGH WORK

MARKS DO NOT WRITE IN THIS MARGIN

ADDITIONAL SPACE FOR ANSWERS AND ROUGH WORK

NATIONAL 5

2017 Specimen Question Paper

SQA ©

HODDER GIBSON
LEARN MORE

N5

National Qualifications SPECIMEN ONLY

S807/75/02

Biology
Section 1—Questions

Date — Not applicable

Duration — 2 hours 30 minutes

Instructions for completion of Section 1 are given on *Page two* of your question and answer booklet S807/75/01.

Record your answers on the answer grid on *Page three* of your question and answer booklet.

Before leaving the examination room you must give your question and answer booklet to the Invigilator; if you do not, you may lose all the marks for this paper.

SECTION 1

1. The diagram shows a single cell.

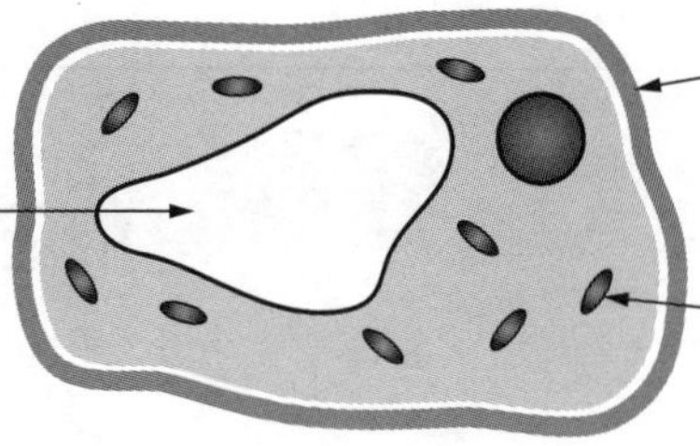

The structure labelled X is made of

A starch
B cellulose
C protein
D phospholipid.

2. Plant cells were placed in a strong salt solution.

Which of the following statements describes the state of the cells and the reason for this?

A Turgid due to water gain.
B Turgid due to water loss.
C Plasmolysed due to water gain.
D Plasmolysed due to water loss.

3. An enzyme reaction takes place because its active site is complementary to

A one type of substrate molecule
B all types of substrate molecule
C one type of product molecule
D all types of product molecules.

4. The diagram shows stages in the production of a substance by genetic engineering.

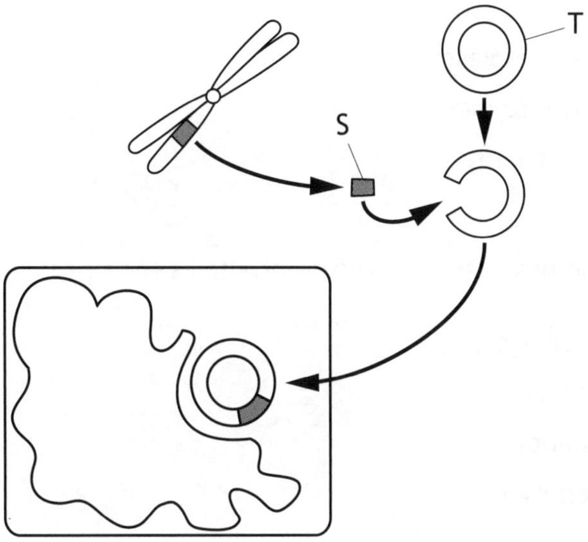

Which row in the table identifies S and T?

	S	T
A	Gene	Plasmid
B	Gene	Bacterium
C	Chromosome	Plasmid
D	Chromosome	Bacterium

5. In the United States of America, 95% of the sugar beet plants grown have been genetically modified (GM).

The simple, whole number ratio of GM plants grown to non-GM plants is

A 20:1

B 1:20

C 19:1

D 1:19

6. Which of the following processes releases energy used to form ATP?

A Muscle cell contraction

B Breakdown of glucose

C Protein synthesis

D Nerve impulse transmission

[Turn over

7. Which of the following statements is **not** true of aerobic respiration?

A Produces carbon dioxide and water

B Begins in the cytoplasm

C Controlled by enzymes

D Requires light energy

8. An individual who possesses two different alleles for a particular gene would display a

A recessive phenotype

B recessive genotype

C dominant phenotype

D dominant genotype.

9. In humans the inheritance of wet or dry earwax is an example of discrete variation.

The allele for wet earwax (E) is dominant to the allele for dry earwax (e).

The diagram shows the inheritance of this characteristic.

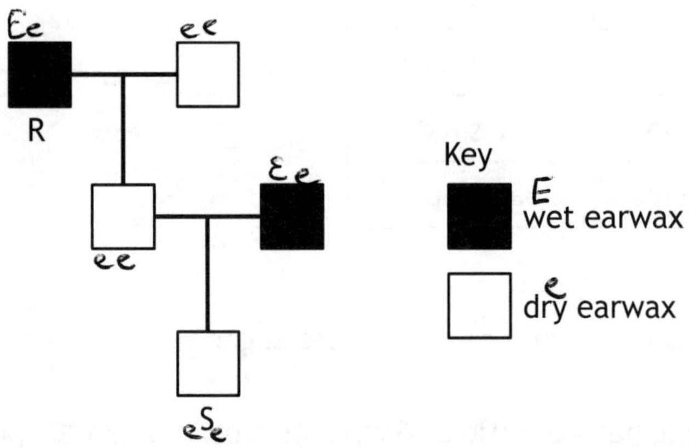

Which row in the table identifies the genotypes of individuals R and S?

	Genotype	
	Individual R	*Individual* S
A	EE	ee
B	Ee	ee
C	Ee	Ee
D	ee	EE

10. Which row in the grid gives correct information about stem cells?

A	Found in embryos	Specialised cells	Cannot self-renew
B	Found in tissues	Specialised cells	Can self-renew
C	Found in embryos	Unspecialised cells	Can self-renew
D	Found in tissues	Unspecialised cells	Cannot self-renew

11. The diagram shows some of the structures in a flower.

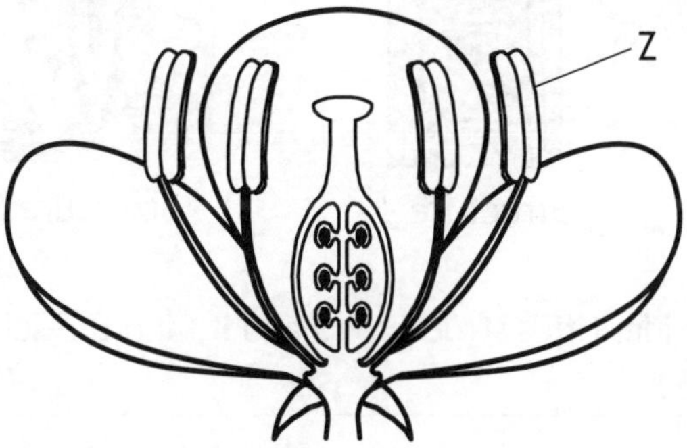

Which of the following is produced in the structure labelled Z?

A Pollen

B Anther

C Ovule

D Ovary

12. Which row in the table identifies the functions of phagocytes and lymphocytes?

	Phagocytes	*Lymphocytes*
A	produce antibodies	engulf pathogens
B	engulf pathogens	engulf pathogens
C	produce antibodies	produce antibodies
D	engulf pathogens	produce antibodies

[Turn over

13. The diagram shows some of the structures involved in transport in plants.

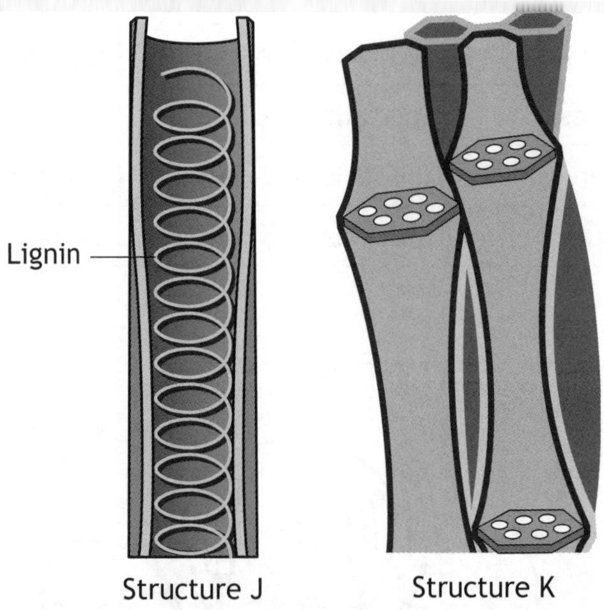

Which row in the table identifies structures J and K, and the substances transported by them?

	Structure J		*Structure K*	
	Name	*Substance transported*	*Name*	*Substance transported*
A	Xylem	Water	Phloem	Sugar
B	Xylem	Sugar	Phloem	Water
C	Phloem	Water	Xylem	Sugar
D	Phloem	Sugar	Xylem	Water

Questions **14** and **15** refer to the diagram of the heart.

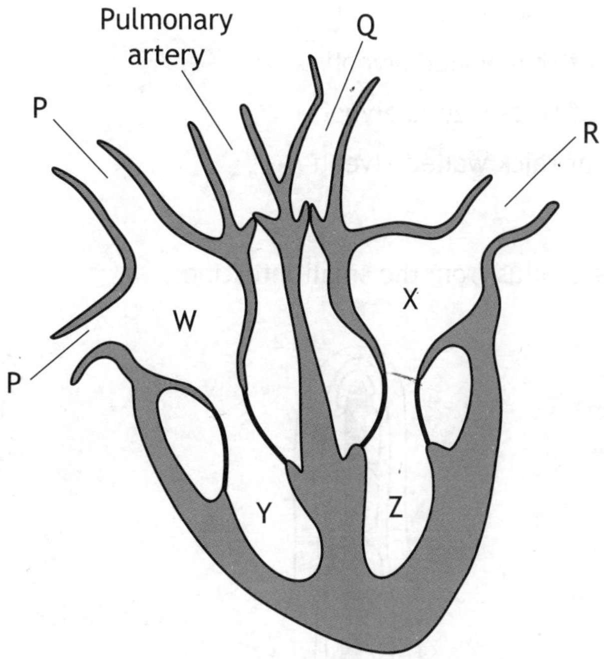

14. Which row in the table identifies the four chambers of the heart labelled W, X, Y and Z?

	W	*X*	*Y*	*Z*
A	Right ventricle	Left ventricle	Right atrium	Left atrium
B	Right ventricle	Left ventricle	Left atrium	Right atrium
C	Right atrium	Left atrium	Left ventricle	Right ventricle
D	Right atrium	Left atrium	Right ventricle	Left ventricle

15. Which row in the table identifies the type of blood carried in blood vessels P, Q and R?

	P	*Q*	*R*
A	deoxygenated	oxygenated	oxygenated
B	deoxygenated	oxygenated	deoxygenated
C	oxygenated	deoxygenated	oxygenated
D	oxygenated	deoxygenated	deoxygenated

16. Which of the following allows efficient gas exchange in the lungs?

A Small number of thin walled alveoli

B Large number of thin walled alveoli

C Small number of thick walled alveoli

D Large number of thick walled alveoli

17. The diagram shows a villus from the small intestine.

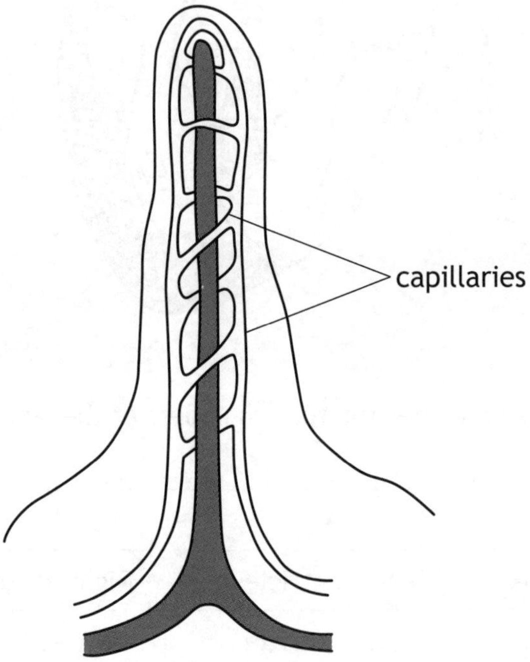

Which food molecules are absorbed into the capillaries of the villus?

A Fatty acids and glycerol

B Amino acids and gycerol

C Amino acids and glucose

D Fatty acids and glucose

18. Which row in the table identifies examples of biotic and abiotic factors?

	Biotic factor	*Abiotic factor*
A	Disease	Rainfall
B	Light intensity	Temperature
C	pH	Soil moisture
D	Predation	Food availability

19. Which of the following statements about a woodland describes a community?

A All the oak trees.

B All the plants.

C All the oak trees and blackbirds.

D All the plants and animals.

20. The diagram shows part of a food web in an oak woodland.

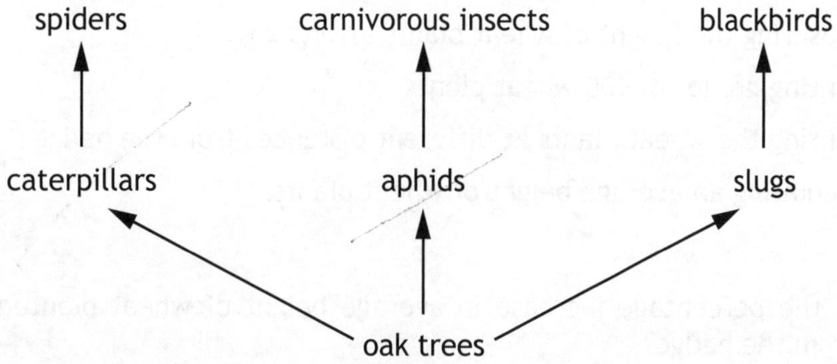

The use of pesticides in a nearby field resulted in the death of most aphids and caterpillars. Which row in the table identifies the effect on the numbers of slugs and carnivorous insects?

	Number of slugs	*Number of carnivorous insects*
A	decreases	stays the same
B	increases	decreases
C	decreases	increases
D	increases	stays the same

Questions **21** and **22** refer to the following information.

An investigation was carried out into the effect of a hedge on the growth of wheat plants.

Groups of 100 wheat plants were planted at different distances from the hedge.

The heights of the wheat plants were measured after six weeks and the results are shown in the table.

Distance planted from hedge (m)	*Average height of wheat plants after six weeks* (cm)
2·0	45
2·5	54
3·0	60
3·5	69
4·0	78
4·5	90

21. The reliability of the results was increased by

A measuring the height of wheat plants after six weeks

B planting groups of 100 wheat plants

C planting the wheat plants at different distances from the hedge

D calculating an average height of wheat plants.

22. What is the percentage increase in average height of wheat planted between 2·0 m and 4·5 m from the hedge?

A 45%

B 50%

C 66%

D 100%

23. Which of the following graphs shows the effects of competition for the same food between a successful species and an unsuccessful species?

A

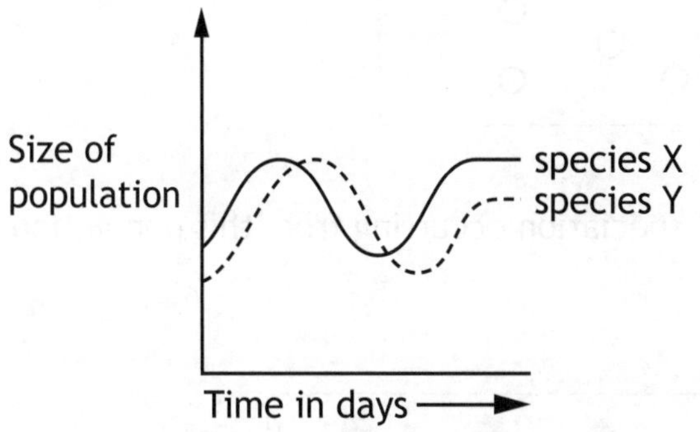

B

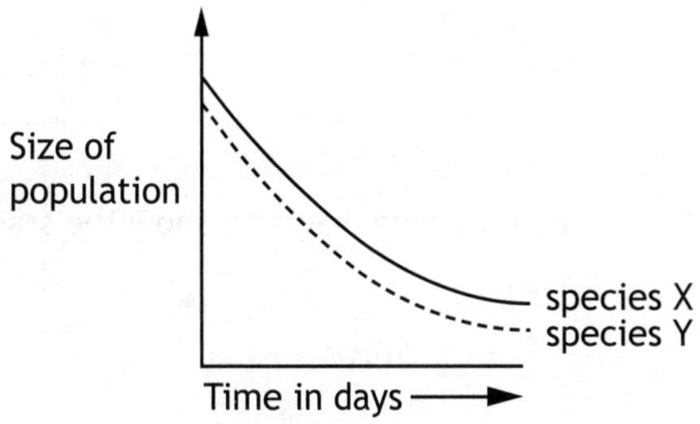

C

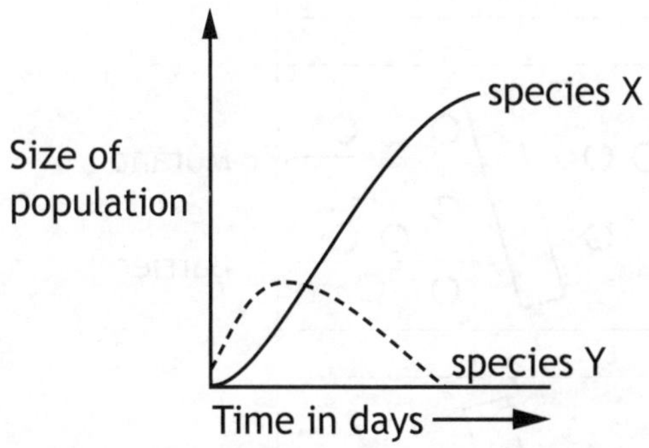

D

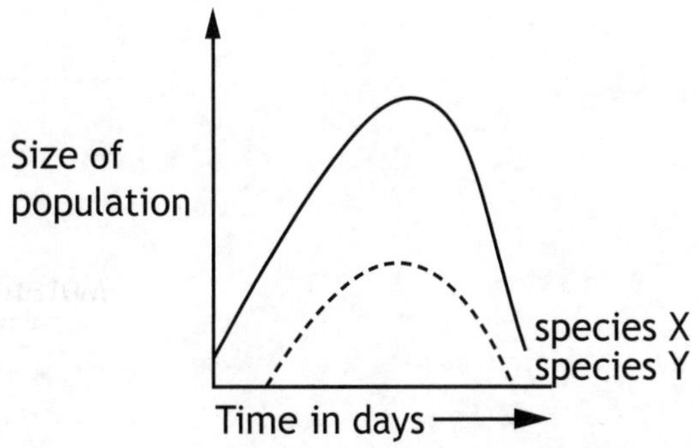

24. Survival of the fittest is also known as

A selection pressure

B natural selection

C selective advantage

D species selection.

[Turn over

25. The diagram represents a population of animals.

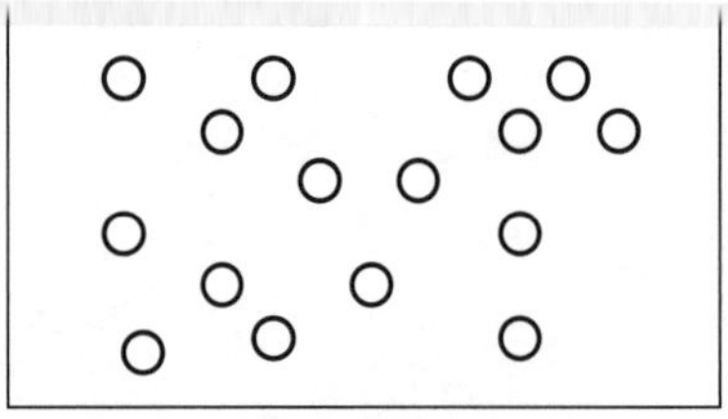

The following diagrams show the stages of speciation occurring from this population.

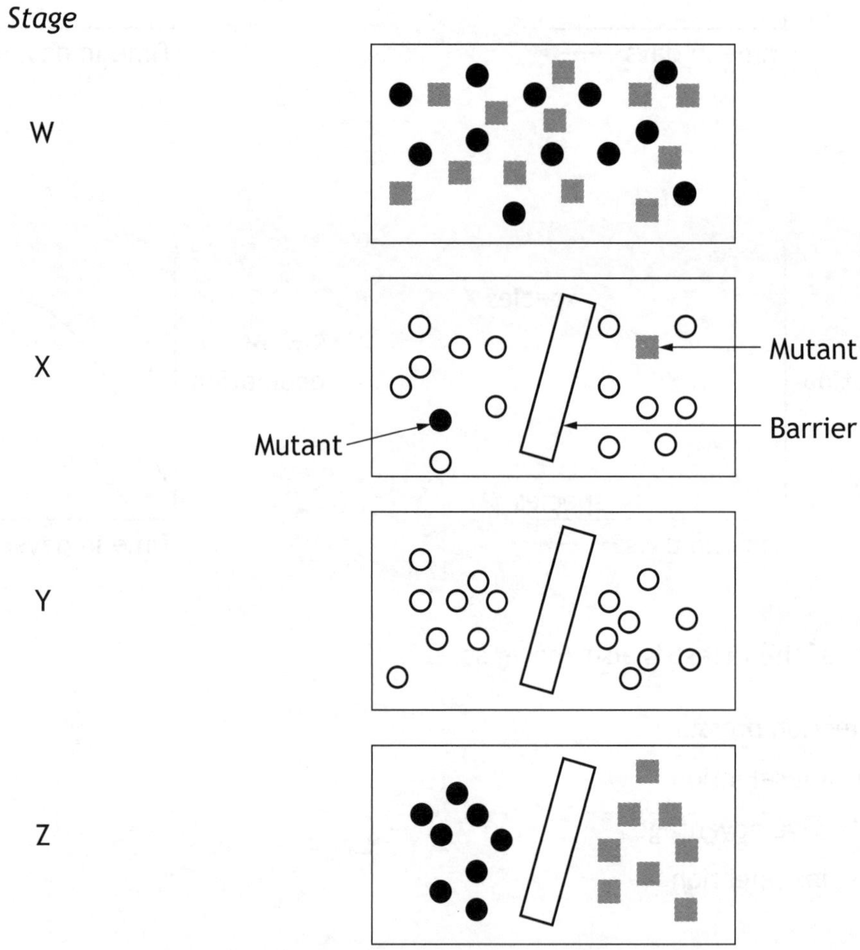

The correct order of the stages of speciation is

A Z, W, X, Y

B Z, X, W, Y

C Y, X, Z, W

D Y, Z, X, W.

[END OF SECTION 1. NOW ATTEMPT THE QUESTIONS IN SECTION 2 OF YOUR QUESTION AND ANSWER BOOKLET]

FOR OFFICIAL USE

N5

National Qualifications
SPECIMEN ONLY

Mark

S807/75/01

Biology
Section 1—Answer Grid and Section 2

Date — Not applicable

Duration — 2 hours 30 minutes

Fill in these boxes and read what is printed below.

Full name of centre

Town

Forename(s)

Surname

Number of seat

Date of birth

Day Month Year

Scottish candidate number

Total marks — 100

SECTION 1 — 25 marks

Attempt ALL questions.

Instructions for completion of Section 1 are given on *Page two*.

SECTION 2 — 75 marks

Attempt ALL questions.

Write your answers clearly in the spaces provided in this booklet. Additional space for answers and rough work is provided at the end of this booklet. If you use this space you must clearly identify the question number you are attempting. Any rough work must be written in this booklet. Score through your rough work when you have written your final copy.

Use **blue** or **black** ink.

Before leaving the examination room you must give this booklet to the Invigilator; if you do not, you may lose all the marks for this paper.

SECTION 1 — 25 marks

The questions for Section 1 are contained in the question paper S807/75/02.

Read these and record your answers on the answer grid on *Page three* opposite.

Use **blue** or **black** ink. Do NOT use gel pens or pencil.

1. The answer to each question is **either** A, B, C or D. Decide what your answer is, then fill in the appropriate bubble (see sample question below).
2. There is **only one correct** answer to each question.
3. Any rough working should be done on the additional space for answers and rough work at the end of this booklet.

Sample Question

The thigh bone is called the

A humerus

B femur

C tibia

D fibula.

The correct answer is **B** — femur. The answer **B** bubble has been clearly filled in (see below).

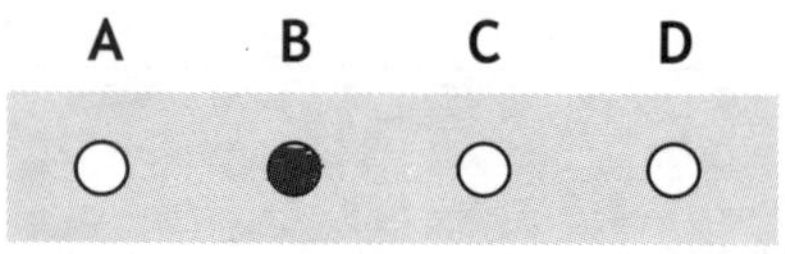

Changing an answer

If you decide to change your answer, cancel your first answer by putting a cross through it (see below) and fill in the answer you want. The answer below has been changed to **D**.

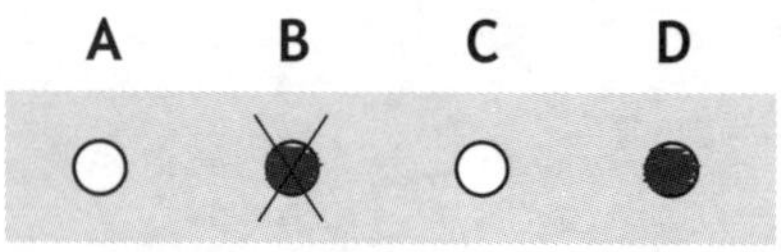

If you then decide to change back to an answer you have already scored out, put a tick (✓) to the **right** of the answer you want, as shown below:

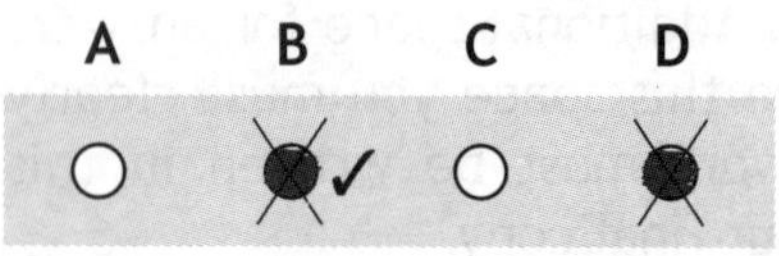

or

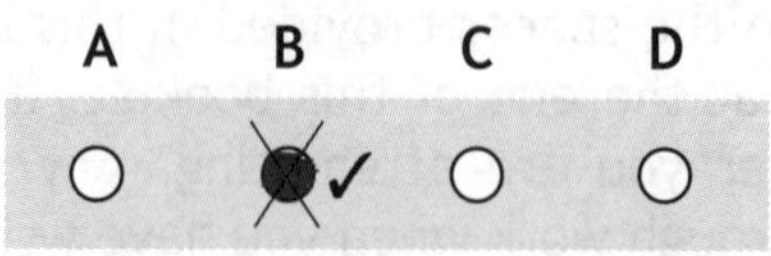

SECTION 1 — Answer Grid

	A	B	C	D
1	○	○	○	○
2	○	○	○	○
3	○	○	○	○
4	○	○	○	○
5	○	○	○	○
6	○	○	○	○
7	○	○	○	○
8	○	○	○	○
9	○	○	○	○
10	○	○	○	○
11	○	○	○	○
12	○	○	○	○
13	○	○	○	○
14	○	○	○	○
15	○	○	○	○
16	○	○	○	○
17	○	○	○	○
18	○	○	○	○
19	○	○	○	○
20	○	○	○	○
21	○	○	○	○
22	○	○	○	○
23	○	○	○	○
24	○	○	○	○
25	○	○	○	○

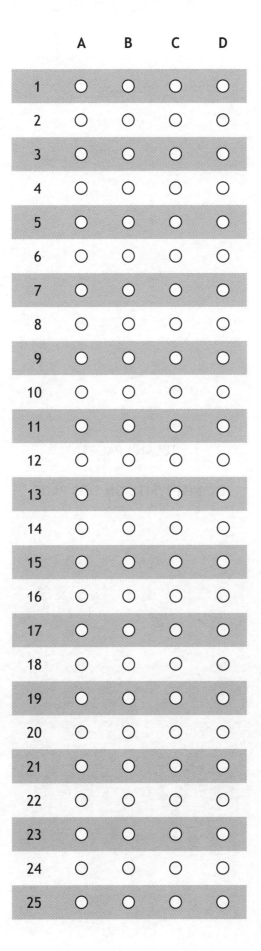

[BLANK PAGE]

DO NOT WRITE ON THIS PAGE

MARKS | DO NOT WRITE IN THIS MARGIN

SECTION 2 — 75 marks

Attempt ALL questions

1. A variegated leaf contains green areas and white areas.

   A student investigated cells from both areas.

   One of these cells is shown.

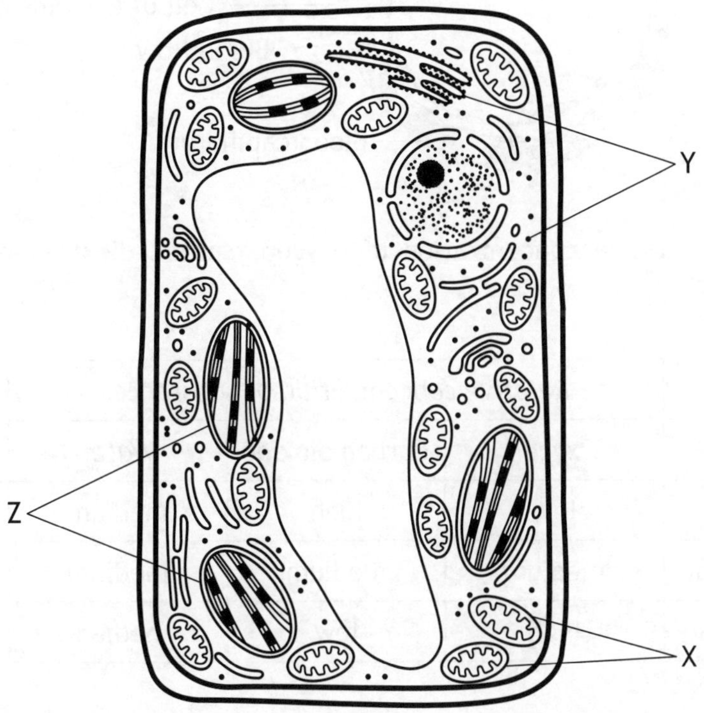

(a) Which letter identifies ribosomes? **1**

____

(b) Give the evidence from the diagram which suggests that this cell produces large quantities of ATP. **1**

____

(c) The student concluded that this cell is from the green area. Explain why this conclusion is correct. **2**

____

____

[Turn over

MARKS | DO NOT WRITE IN THIS MARGIN

2. The diagram shows a site of gas exchange in the lungs.

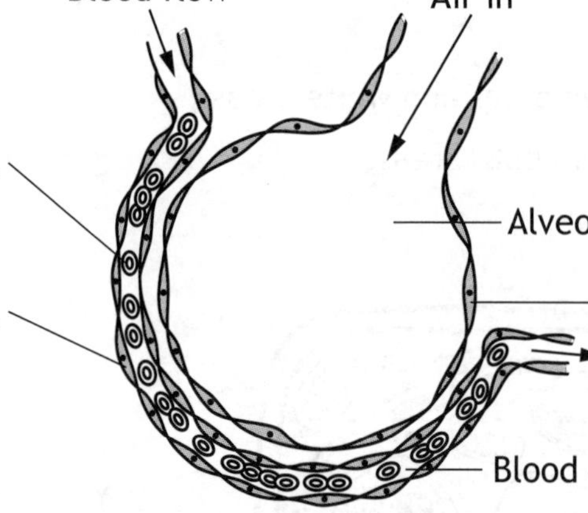

The table shows the relative concentration of oxygen, carbon dioxide and water in three cell types.

	Relative concentration of substances		
Cell Type	*Oxygen*	*Carbon dioxide*	*Water*
Red blood cell	low	high	medium
Cell of capillary wall	medium	medium	medium
Cell of alveolus wall	high	low	medium

(a) (i) Describe the pathway that oxygen would take when moving between these cell types. **1**

(ii) Explain why oxygen moves along this pathway. **1**

(b) Osmosis would not occur between the cells of the capillary wall and the cells of the alveolus wall. **1**

Using the information provided, explain why this is the case.

MARKS | DO NOT WRITE IN THIS MARGIN

3. The diagram shows how genetic information in the nucleus is used in the first stage of making a protein.

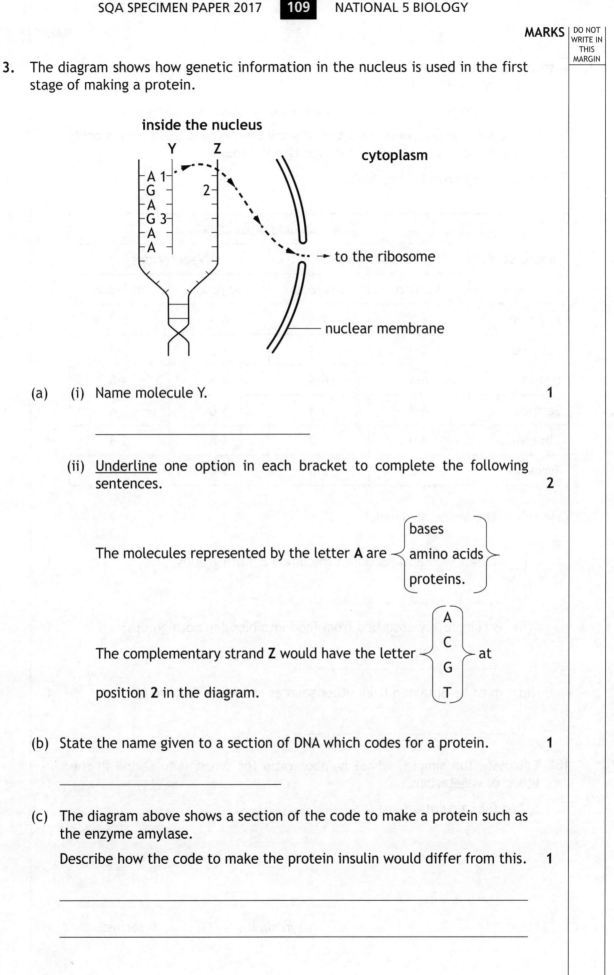

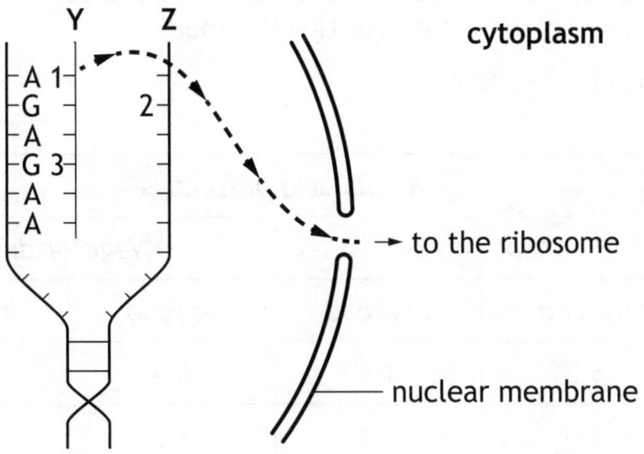

(a) (i) Name molecule Y. **1**

____

(ii) Underline one option in each bracket to complete the following sentences. **2**

The molecules represented by the letter **A** are { bases / amino acids / proteins. }

The complementary strand **Z** would have the letter { A / C / G / T } at position **2** in the diagram.

(b) State the name given to a section of DNA which codes for a protein. **1**

____

(c) The diagram above shows a section of the code to make a protein such as the enzyme amylase.

Describe how the code to make the protein insulin would differ from this. **1**

____

____

MARKS DO NOT WRITE IN THIS MARGIN

4. A study was carried out into the percentage of amino acids present in the blood of people with different diets.

One group tested were meat eaters and the other group were vegetarians.

In both groups, samples were analysed to show the percentage of amino acids in their food and in their blood after digesting the food.

The results are shown in the table.

Amino acid	*Amino acid present* (%)			
	Meat eaters		*Vegetarians*	
	In food	*In blood*	*In food*	*In blood*
Arginine	5·5	1·6	6·4	1·4
Leucine	8·0	5·4	7·0	5·0
Lysine	6·4	6·4	4·8	4·8
Serine	4·8	5·4	5·0	5·4
Threonine	4·0	3·8	3·8	3·8
Tyrosine	3·2	2·0	3·0	1·8

(a) Select the amino acid which

(i) is least well absorbed into the blood in both groups; **1**

____

(ii) is completely absorbed from food into blood in both groups; **1**

____

(iii) must be obtained from other sources as well as from food. **1**

____

(b) Calculate the simple, whole number ratio for tyrosine to serine in the blood of vegetarians. **1**

Space for calculation

____________ : ____________

tyrosine *serine*

MARKS DO NOT WRITE IN THIS MARGIN

4. (continued)

(c) On the grid below, add a scale and complete the remaining 5 bars to show the percentage of amino acids in the **blood of both groups.** 2

(An additional grid, if required, can be found on *Page twenty-nine*)

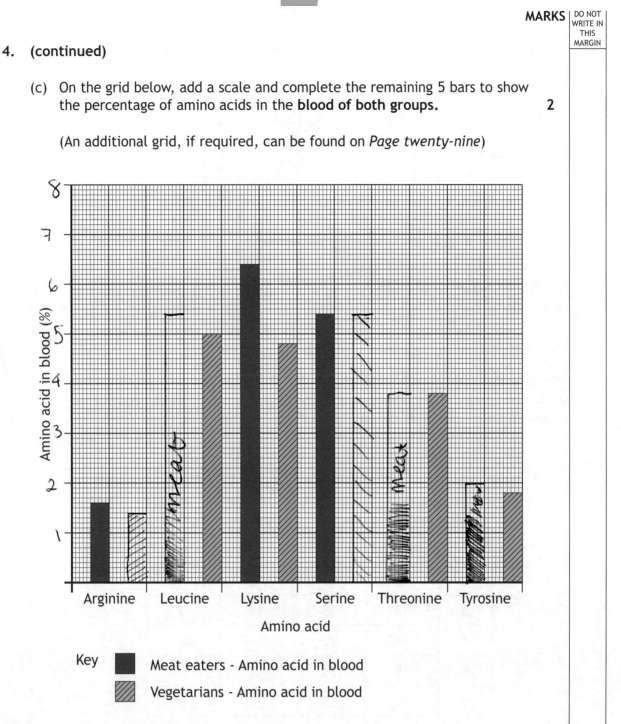

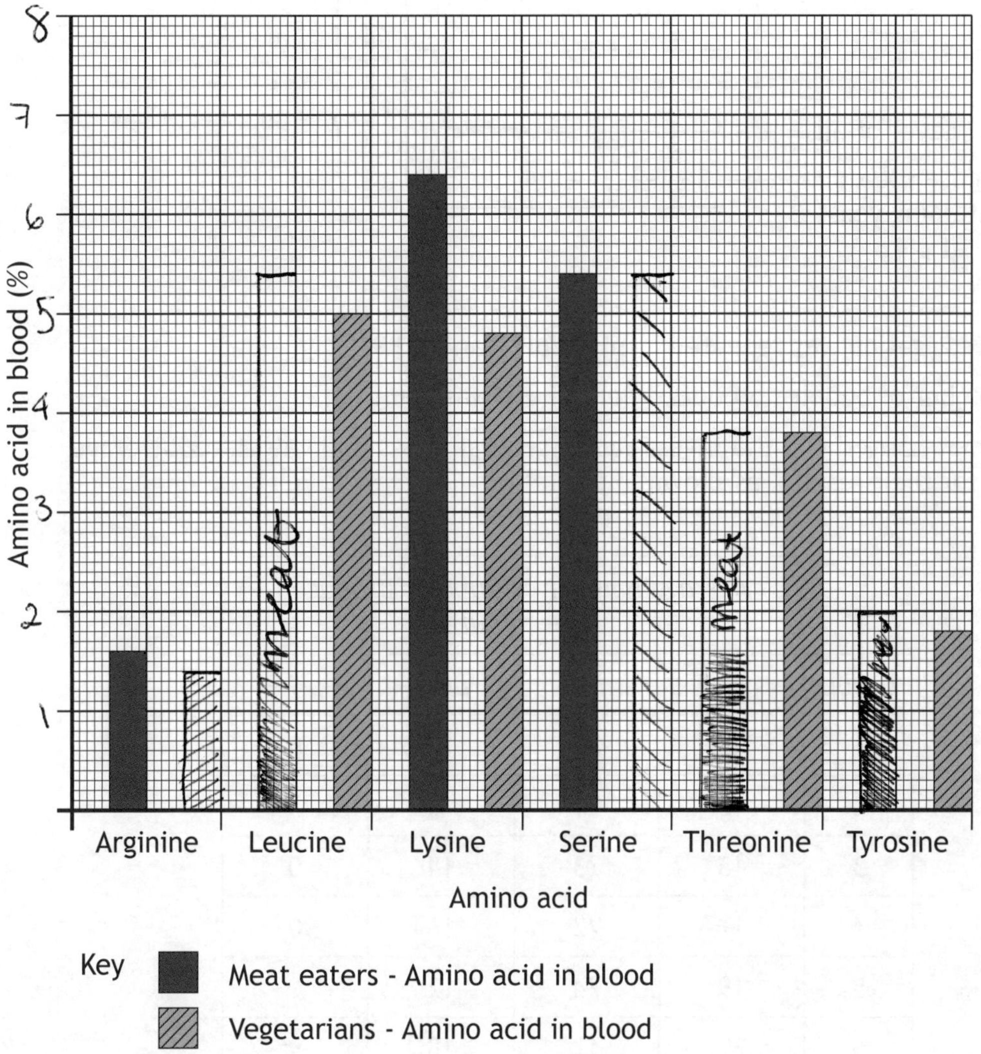

[Turn over

MARKS DO NOT WRITE IN THIS MARGIN

5. An investigation was carried out to find the effect of pH on fermentation by yeast, using the apparatus shown.

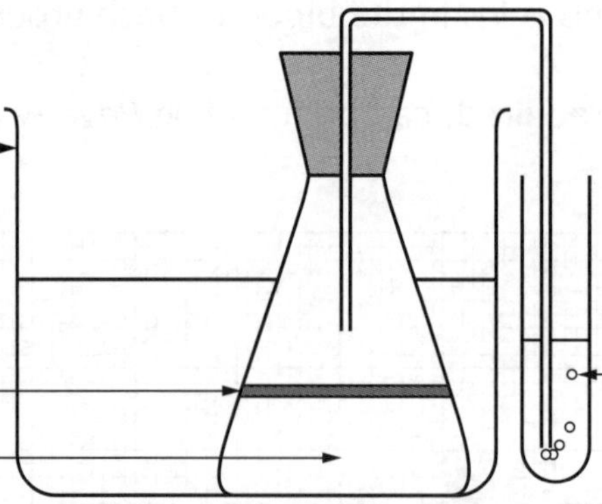

The investigation was repeated at pH 3, pH 7 and pH 9.

The number of bubbles produced per minute was counted.

Six groups carried out the investigation several times and calculated average values for their results, as shown in the table.

	Average number of bubbles produced per minute			
Group	*pH 3*	*pH 5*	*pH 7*	*pH 9*
1	8	25	17	0
2	10	21	13	3
3	15	23	14	0
4	17	22	16	0
5	19	24	12	1
6	22	17	18	9

(a) Name the gas produced during fermentation in yeast. 1

____

(b) From the table, identify the optimum pH for fermentation by yeast and give a reason for your choice.

pH ______ 1

Reason ______________________________ 1

MARKS DO NOT WRITE IN THIS MARGIN

5. (continued)

(c) This investigation could be adapted to find the effect of a variable other than pH.

Choose **one** variable from the list.

Describe **two** ways that the apparatus would be adapted to demonstrate the effect of this variable. **2**

List

Type of yeast

Temperature

Concentration of glucose solution

Variable ______________________________

Adaptation 1 ______________________________

____

Adaptation 2 ______________________________

____

[Turn over

MARKS | DO NOT WRITE IN THIS MARGIN

6. The diagrams show a cell in different stages of mitosis.

A B C D E

(a) Use letters from the diagrams to complete the correct order of the stages. **1**

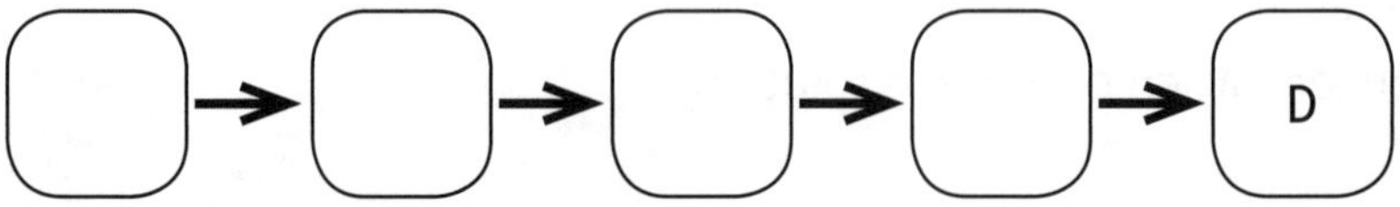

(b) Describe what is happening in stage C. **1**

____

____

(c) Explain why it is important for the new cells produced to be identical to the original cell. **1**

____

____

(d) Calculate the number of times the original cell would have to divide to form 128 cells in total. **1**

Space for calculation

______________ times

MARKS | DO NOT WRITE IN THIS MARGIN

7. (a) The diagram shows a hormone, such as insulin, binding with its target cell.

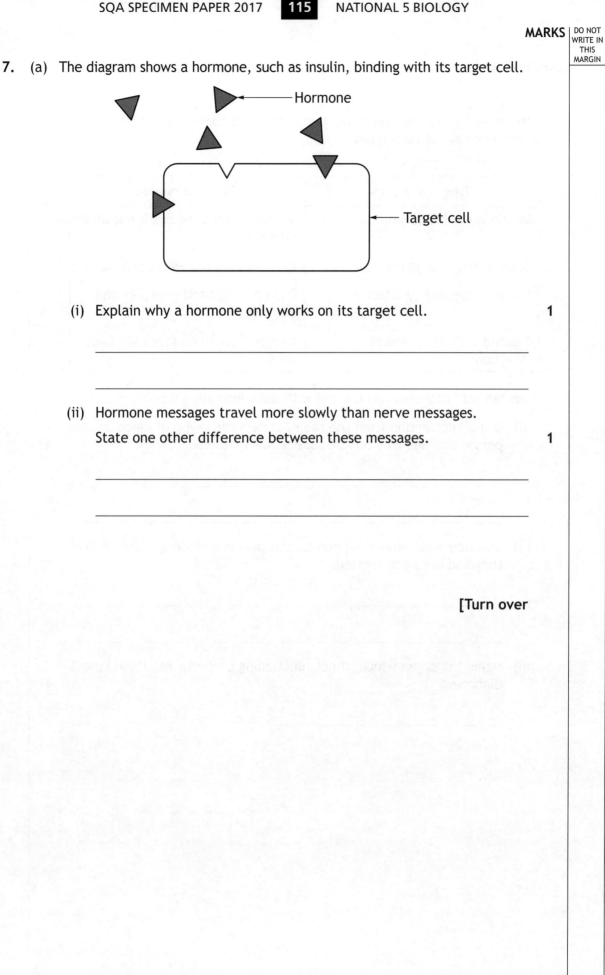

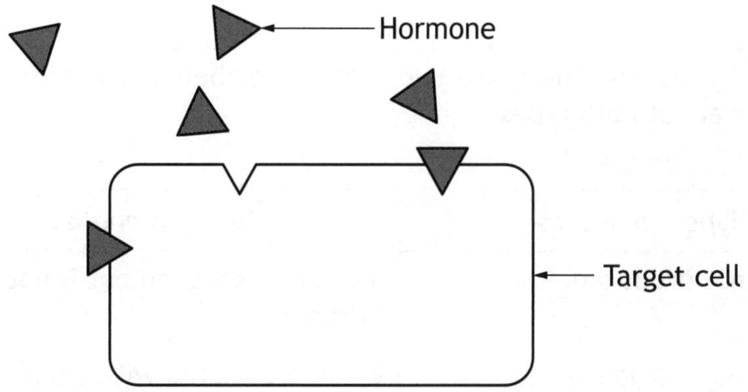

(i) Explain why a hormone only works on its target cell. **1**

___

___

(ii) Hormone messages travel more slowly than nerve messages.
State one other difference between these messages. **1**

___

___

[Turn over

MARKS | DO NOT WRITE IN THIS MARGIN

7. **(continued)**

(b) Diabetes is a condition in which the blood glucose level is not fully controlled by insulin. There are two types of diabetes. The table shows information about both types.

Type 1 diabetes	*Type 2 diabetes*
Insulin is not produced	Insulin is produced but is not used effectively
Often starts at a young age	Often associated with being obese
Can be triggered by infection	Can be controlled with diet and exercise
Treated with daily insulin injections	Medication can be given in tablet form

A person with diabetes was treated with daily insulin injections.

(i) Using information from the table, state which type of diabetes this person had and why this treatment was required. 1

(ii) Describe what would happen to this person's blood glucose level if they had not been treated. 1

(iii) Name the organ which, if not functioning properly, results in type 1 diabetes. 1

MARKS DO NOT WRITE IN THIS MARGIN

8. Hair type in humans is genetically controlled.

The dominant form is curly hair (H). The recessive form (h) produces straight hair.

Both parents of this curly-haired child have the genotype Hh.

(a) State the term used to describe the genotype of both parents. 1

____

(b) Complete the Punnett square to show the possible genotypes of their offspring. 1

Male gametes

		H	h
Female gametes	H		
	h		

(c) Give the possible genotypes of the girl in the picture. 1

____

[Turn over

MARKS DO NOT WRITE IN THIS MARGIN

9. An experiment was set up as shown to measure the transpiration rate of a plant at room temperature. The mass was recorded at the start and again after 6 hours. The results are shown in the table.

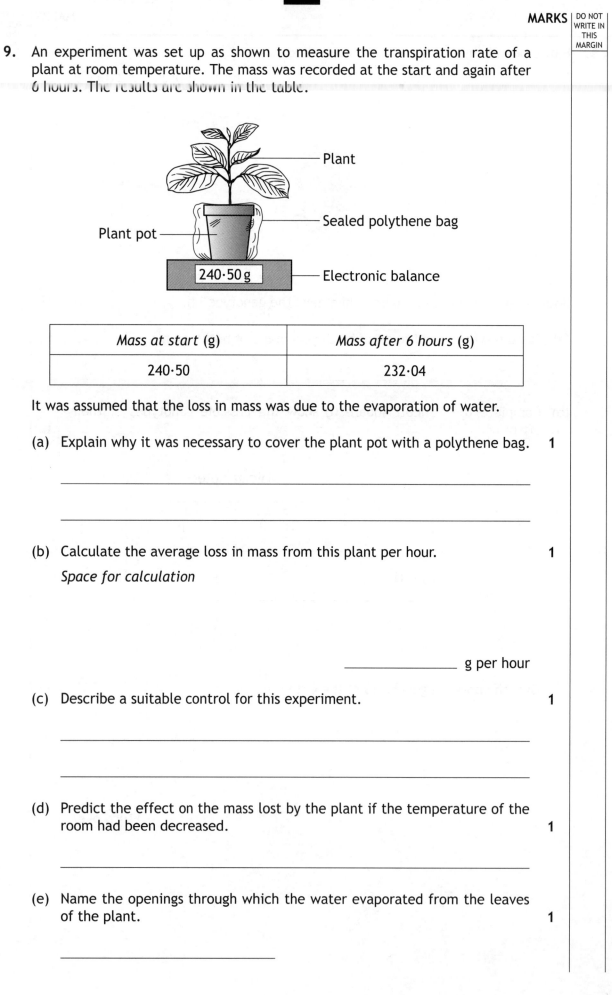

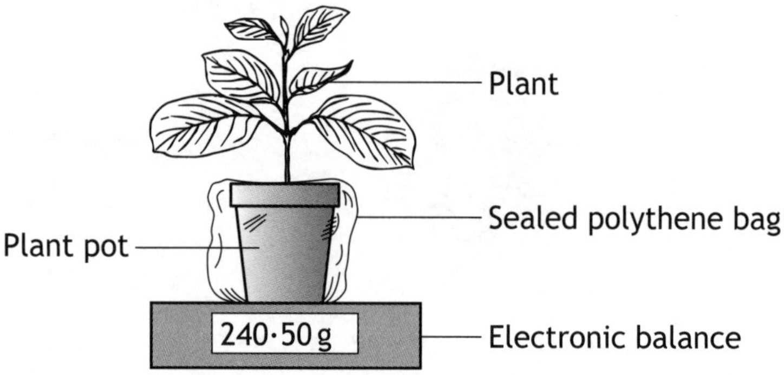

Mass at start (g)	*Mass after 6 hours* (g)
240·50	232·04

It was assumed that the loss in mass was due to the evaporation of water.

(a) Explain why it was necessary to cover the plant pot with a polythene bag. **1**

(b) Calculate the average loss in mass from this plant per hour. **1**

Space for calculation

_______ g per hour

(c) Describe a suitable control for this experiment. **1**

(d) Predict the effect on the mass lost by the plant if the temperature of the room had been decreased. **1**

(e) Name the openings through which the water evaporated from the leaves of the plant. **1**

MARKS DO NOT WRITE IN THIS MARGIN

10. (a) Blood travels in three types of blood vessels.

Compare the structure of **two** of these types of vessels. **3**

(b) State the function of haemoglobin found in red blood cells. **1**

[Turn over

MARKS | DO NOT WRITE IN THIS MARGIN

11. (a) Cichlid fish are all found in Lake Malawi in Africa.

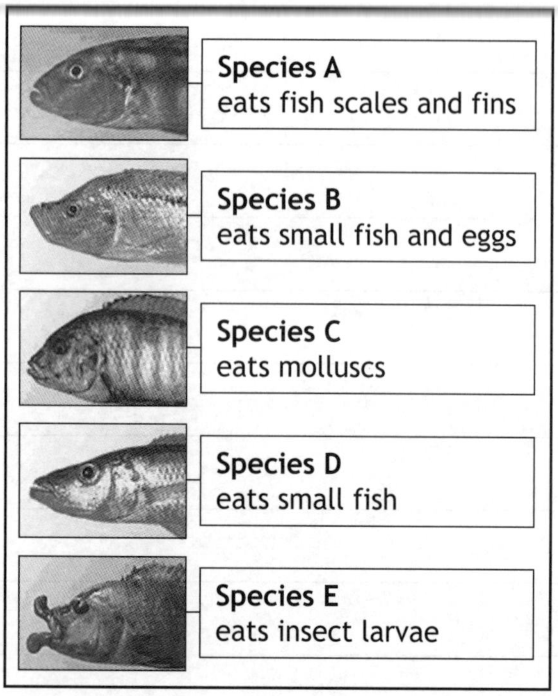

(i) Using the information shown, identify the feature which enables Cichlid fish to have different diets. **1**

____

(ii) Predict **two** species of Cichlid which would be in competition with each other if there was a shortage of fish eggs. **1**

Species ______________ and ______________

(b) State the term which describes the role that an organism, such as the Cichlid fish, plays within its community. **1**

____

MARKS | DO NOT WRITE IN THIS MARGIN

11. (continued)

(c) Fresh water environments, such as Lake Malawi, can be affected by the overuse of fertilisers. This can impact on the organisms living in these environments.

The following statements show how this might occur, but not in the correct order.

1. Chemicals leach into water
2. Fish die
3. Overuse of fertilisers
4. Oxygen levels decrease
5. Algal bloom develops

Place a statement number in each box to complete the sequence of events. **1**

3				

(d) A fresh water environment is an example of an ecosystem.

Describe what is meant by the term ecosystem. **1**

____

____

[Turn over

MARKS | DO NOT WRITE IN THIS MARGIN

12. (a) Photosynthesis is the process by which plants produce sugar using light.

The flow diagram represents some stages of photosynthesis in a leaf.

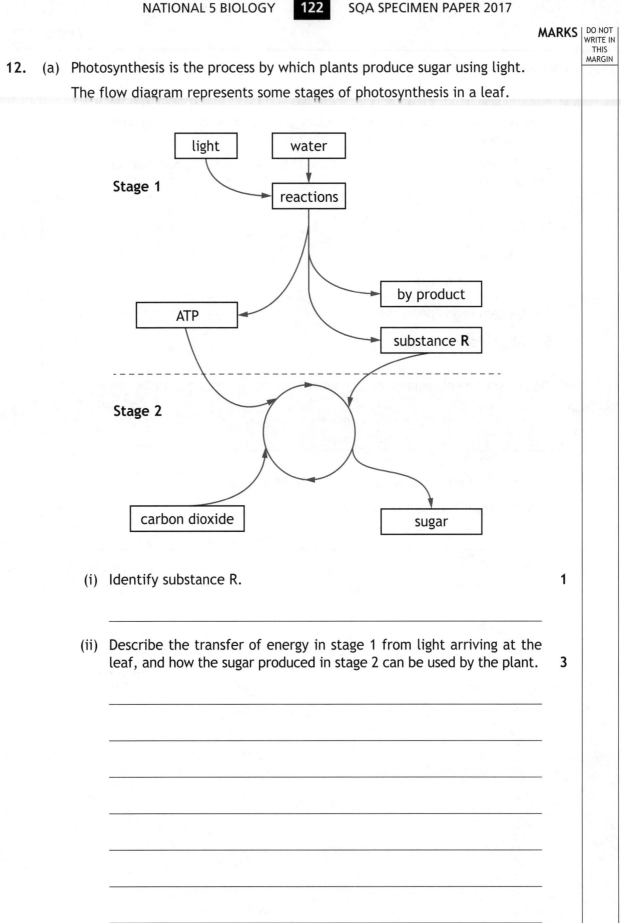

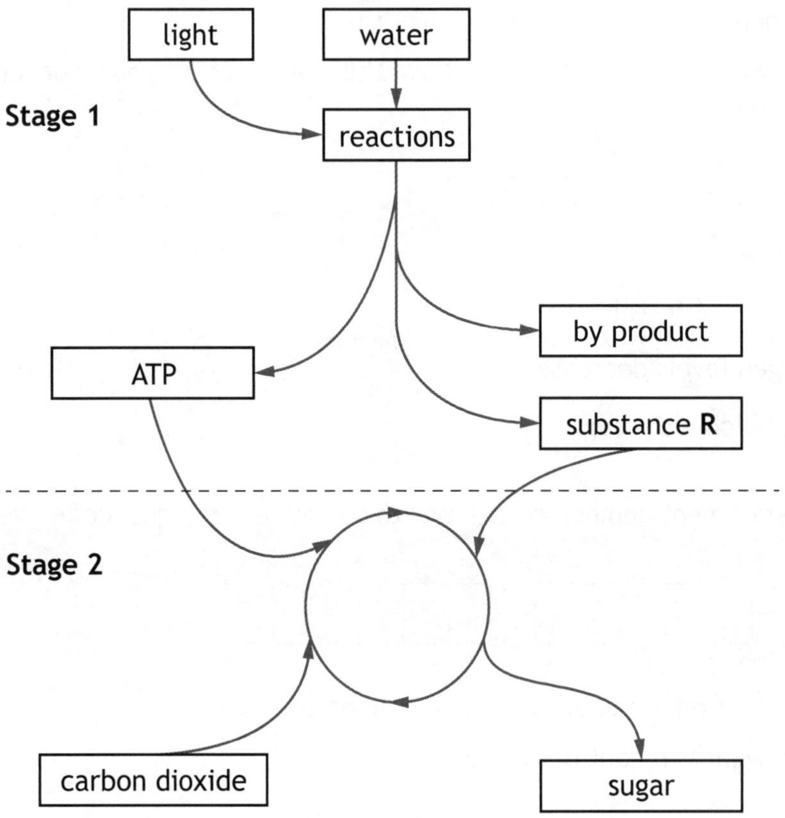

(i) Identify substance R. **1**

____

(ii) Describe the transfer of energy in stage 1 from light arriving at the leaf, and how the sugar produced in stage 2 can be used by the plant. **3**

____

____

____

____

____

____

____

____

MARKS DO NOT WRITE IN THIS MARGIN

12. (continued)

(b) The graph shows the effect of light intensity and carbon dioxide concentration on the rate of photosynthesis.

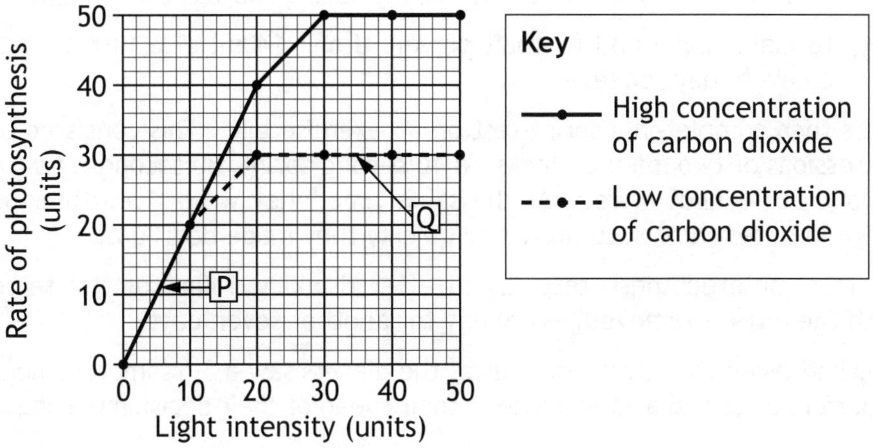

Identify the limiting factor at each of the points P and Q. **2**

P ___________________________________

Q ___________________________________

[Turn over

MARKS DO NOT WRITE IN THIS MARGIN

Adapted from, Herald, Saturday 19th September 2015

13. Beetroot Juice

Scientists have a theory that drinking nitrate-rich beetroot juice has an effect on both sprint performance and decision making during sports.

In a study, 16 male rugby and football players drank 140ml of a nitrate-rich beetroot juice every day for seven days.

The players then completed a sprint test on an exercise bike. This consisted of repeated sessions of two minute blocks - a 10 second sprint, 80 seconds of slow pedalling and 30 seconds of rest. At the same time, they were given thinking tasks designed to test how accurately and quickly they made decisions.

The players completed these tests again after drinking 140ml of the same juice, with the nitrate removed, every day for another seven days.

When they had taken the nitrate-rich juice, the players saw a 3·5% improvement in sprint performance and a 3% increase in their speed of their decision making.

The improvement may seem small, but it could mean the players are able to make important decisions faster and cover more ground than their opponents in the seconds when it matters most.

(a) Suggest the aim of the research described in the passage. 1

____

____

(b) A dependent variable is what scientists measure or observe as a result of the changes they make in their investigation.

Identify the dependent variable in this investigation. 1

____

MARKS DO NOT WRITE IN THIS MARGIN

13. (continued)

(c) Complete the table, with suitable headings, to show the activities and timings of the two minute sprint test. **2**

(An additional table, if required, can be found on *Page twenty-nine*)

Activities on te bike	Time spent doing activities (sec)
sprint slow pedalling rest thinking tasks	10 80 30 Throught bike session.

(d) What conclusion did the scientists draw from this study? **1**

(e) Give a reason why it could be suggested that the results of the investigation might be unreliable. **1**

[Turn over

MARKS | DO NOT WRITE IN THIS MARGIN

14. (a) A food chain is shown along with three pyramids of numbers.

grass ⟶ zebra ⟶ lion ⟶ flea

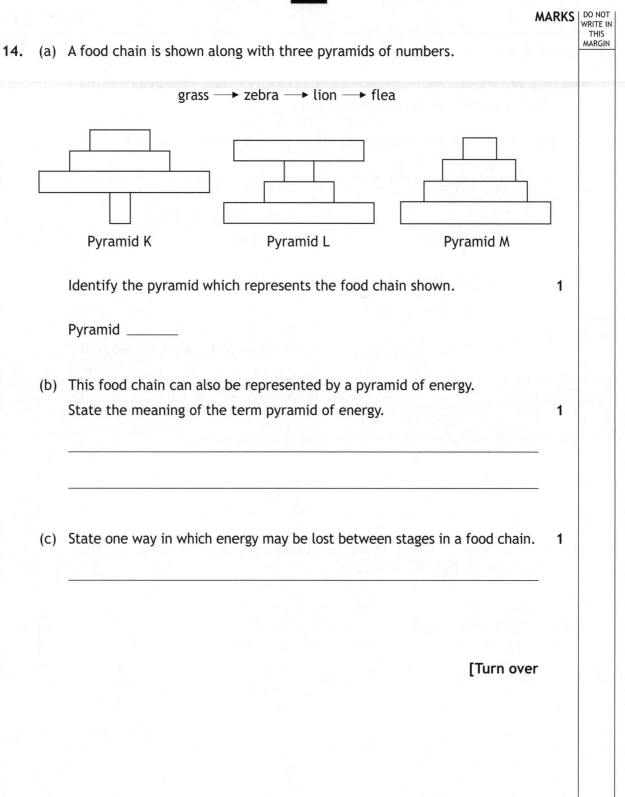

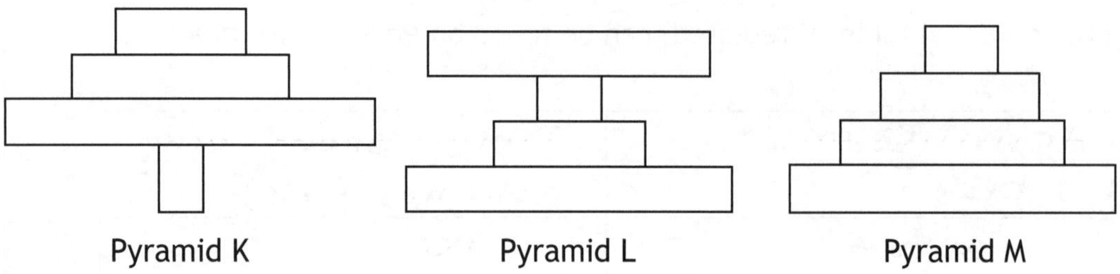

Identify the pyramid which represents the food chain shown. **1**

Pyramid _______

(b) This food chain can also be represented by a pyramid of energy.

State the meaning of the term pyramid of energy. **1**

____

____

(c) State one way in which energy may be lost between stages in a food chain. **1**

____

[Turn over

MARKS DO NOT WRITE IN THIS MARGIN

15. The number of farmland birds in Europe has decreased dramatically in recent years. A study estimated that the total bird population has dropped from 600 million to 300 million between 1980 and 2009.

It has been suggested that the use of pesticides may have killed many of the insects that are eaten by bird species.

The effect on the populations of some bird species is shown in the table.

Bird species	*Population in 1980* (millions)	*Population in 2009* (millions)	*Population decrease* (%)
Linnet	37·0	14·0	62
Meadow pipit	34·9	12·9	63
Corn bunting	27·2	9·2	66
Starling	84·9	39·9	53
Whinchat	10·4	3·4	67
Yellow wagtail	9·4	4·4	53

(a) Explain why the population decrease was expressed as a percentage rather than a decrease in number. **1**

____

____

(b) Using information from **the passage and the table**, calculate the percentage of Meadow pipit in the total bird population in 2009. **1**

Space for calculation

________________ %

(c) Identify the two species of birds which were least affected between 1980 and 2009. **1**

________________ and ________________

16. A group of students wanted to investigate the effect of various factors on the distribution of the plant Yellow Iris.

They set up a line transect and marked out five evenly spaced sample sites. The abundance of Yellow Iris was recorded, and values for soil temperature, pH and moisture were measured at the same sample sites.

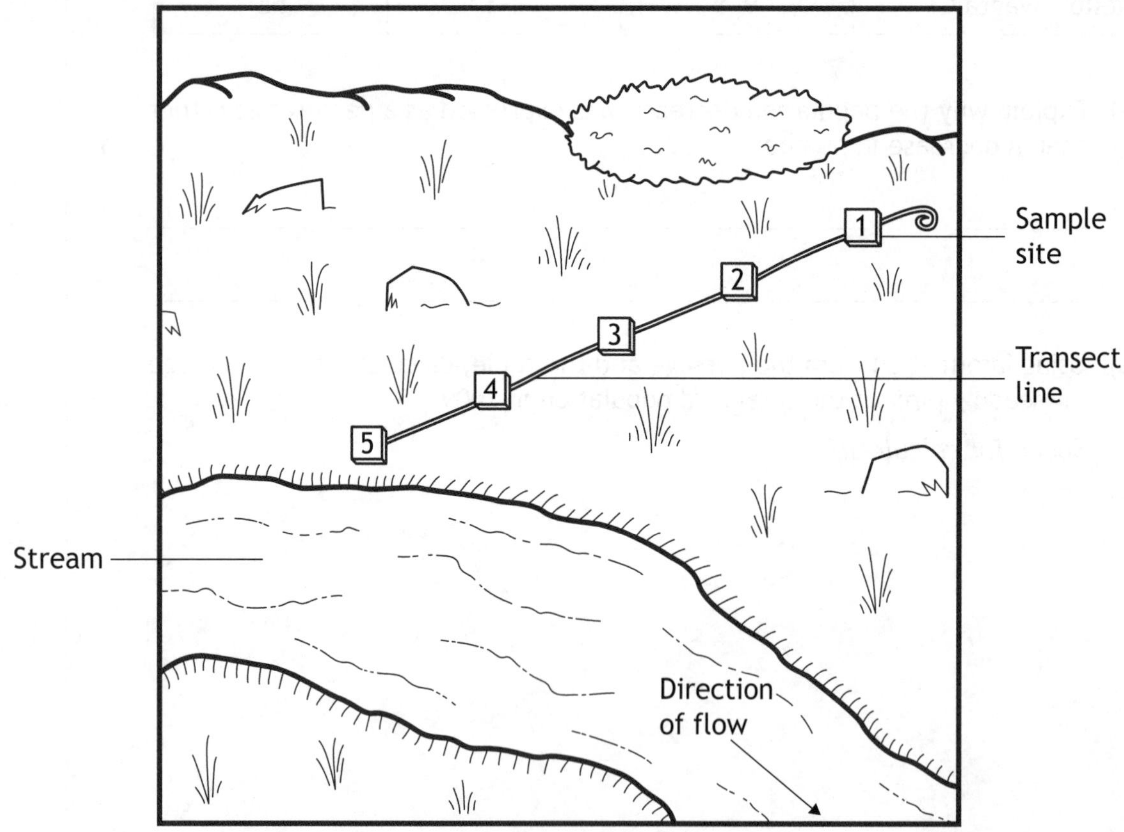

MARKS DO NOT WRITE IN THIS MARGIN

16. (continued)

The results are shown in the table.

Sample site	*Soil temperature* (°C)	*Soil moisture* (% saturation)	*Soil pH*	*Yellow Iris abundance*
1	12	15	5·4	0
2	13	39	5·5	3
3	11	56	5·6	9
4	12	78	5·5	21
5	11	90	5·4	25

(a) Describe the distribution of Yellow Iris along the transect line from sample site 1 to 5. **1**

(b) Identify which abiotic factor had the greatest effect on the distribution of Yellow Iris. **1**

(c) Probes were used to measure the soil moisture and soil pH.

Describe a precaution that should be taken when using a probe to make sure that the measurements are valid. **1**

[Turn over for next question

MARKS DO NOT WRITE IN THIS MARGIN

17. The table shows some features of common seaweeds.

Seaweed	Colour	Shape	Bladders
Bladder wrack	brown	branched	present in pairs
Cladophora	green	long and thin	absent
Spiral wrack	brown	twisted	present in pairs
Channel wrack	brown	grooved edges	absent
Egg wrack	brown	branched	present along its length
Sea lettuce	green	flat	absent
Serrated wrack	brown	saw-toothed edge	absent

(a) Use the information in the table to complete the key. **3**

1.	Green seaweed	go to 2
	Brown seaweed	go to 3
2.	Flat	Sea lettuce
	long & thin	Cladophora
3.	Bladders present	go to 4
	Bladders absent	go to 6
4.	Bladders along its length	Egg wrack
	Bladders in pairs	go to 5
5.	Twisted	Spiral wrack
	Branched	Bladder wrack
6.	Grooved edge	Channel wrack
	Saw-toothed edge	Serrated wrack

(b) Describe the difference that would allow a person to identify a piece of seaweed as Egg wrack or Bladder wrack. **1**

____

____

(c) Identify a feature which Cladophora and Serrated wrack have in common. **1**

____

[END OF SPECIMEN QUESTION PAPER]

ADDITIONAL SPACE FOR ANSWERS

Additional grid for Question 4 (c)

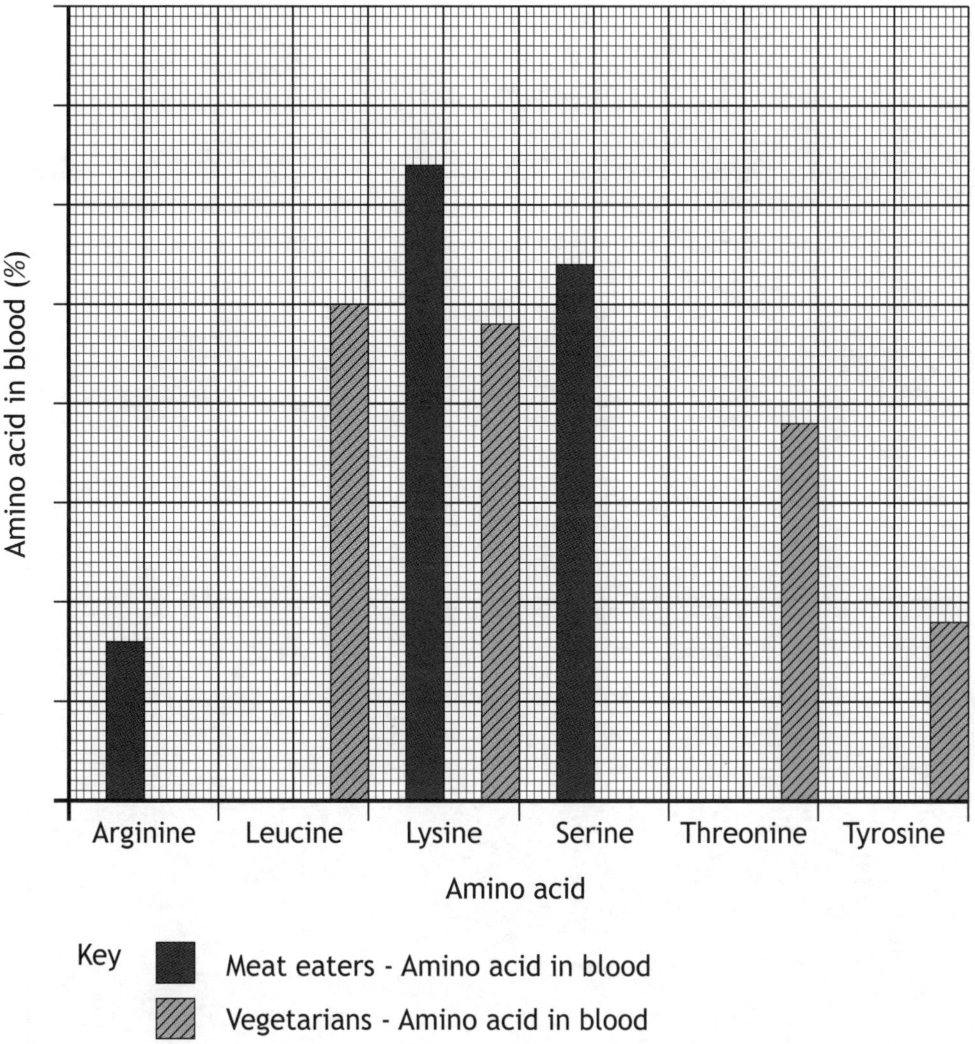

Additional table for Question 13 (c)

MARKS DO NOT WRITE IN THIS MARGIN

ADDITIONAL SPACE FOR ANSWERS

NATIONAL 5

Answers

SQA ©

HODDER GIBSON
LEARN MORE

ANSWERS FOR

SQA NATIONAL 5 BIOLOGY 2017

NATIONAL 5 BIOLOGY 2016

SECTION 1

Question	Response
1.	B
2.	A
3.	B
4.	D
5.	C
6.	C
7.	A
8.	C
9.	A
10.	B
11.	B
12.	C
13.	C
14.	B
15.	D
16.	B
17.	C
18.	A
19.	D
20.	D

SECTION 2

1. (a) Selectively permeable/semi-permeable/(contains) proteins/(phospho)lipids/protein channels/protein carriers

   (b) (i) Leaf:
   - cell swells/becomes turgid (or suitable description of turgid)

   Red blood cell:
   - cell swells/bursts/may burst

   (ii) 1. Diffusion/active transport
   2. Definition:
   Diffusion – Movement of molecules/particles from a high to a low concentration
   OR
   down the concentration gradient
   Active Transport – Movement of molecules/ions from a low to a high concentration
   OR
   against/up the concentration gradient

2. (a) (i) Degradation **(1)**
   Substrate **(1)**

   (ii) **Prediction** – (All or some) lactose would not be removed from the milk/milk would contain lactose/it would not be lactose free **(1)**
   Explanation – Enzyme/lactase denatured
   OR
   Enzyme/active site has changed shape/description of change of shape **(1)**

   (b) Speed up (chemical/biological/biochemical) reactions/allow reactions to occur at lower temperatures/lower the activation energy

   (c) Protein/amino acids

3. (a) (i) Plasmid
   (ii) 2

   (b) (i) To ensure there are no other microbes/bacteria (or equivalent) present
   OR
   To prevent/stop contamination/cross-contamination/growth of other cultures
   (ii) Temperature/pH/O_2 or CO_2 concentration/nutrient or food levels

4. (a) (i) Requires/uses/needs a lot of energy/ATP
   AND
   For movement/contraction
   (ii) Carbon dioxide/Water/(38) ATP

   (b) Glucose converted/broken down to pyruvate/pyruvic acid **(1)**
   Pyruvate/pyruvic acid converted to lactic acid **(1)**
   (2) ATP produced **(1)**

5. (a) (i)

Type of blood vessel	
vein	(1)
artery	(1)

   (ii) They have thinnest/thinner wall(s)

   (b) Coronary artery/arteries

6. (a)

Individual	*Possible Genotype(s)*	*Phenotype*	
A	Tt		(1)
B			
C		Hitchhiker's (thumb)	(1)

   (b) (i) 13:5
   (ii) Fertilisation is a random process
   OR
   Numbers in sample too small

7. (a) (i) increase in humidity - decreases

   increase in temperature - increases

   increase in wind speed - increases

   (ii) **humidity**
   put the apparatus in a (transparent) bag/container
   temperature
   put a heater beside it/put in a water bath at a higher temperature
   wind speed
   use a fan/hairdryer on cool setting beside the apparatus

(b) (i) P has a greater number of stomata/Q has fewer stomata
(ii) Guard (cells)

8. (a) Medium (salt)

(b)

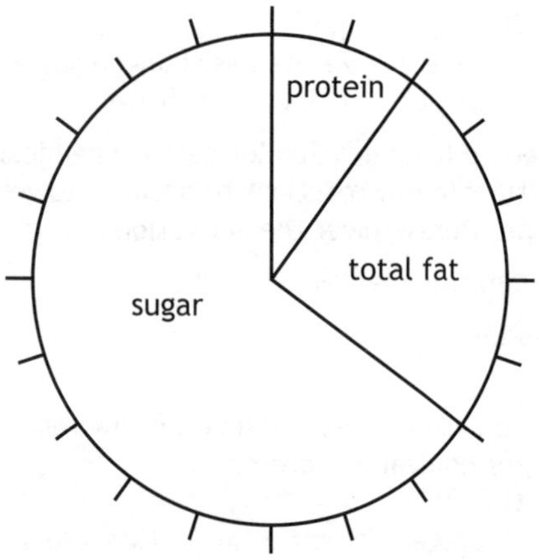

(1 mark for divisions, 1 mark for labels)

(c) (i) 80
(ii) 8400

9. (a) They have receptors/receptor proteins

AND

these are specific/match this hormone

(b) Endocrine

(c) Glucagon

10. (a) (i) Stickleback
(ii) Perch

(b) Heat/movement/undigested material/faeces/excrement/fur/bones/hair

11. (a) (i) 30
(ii)

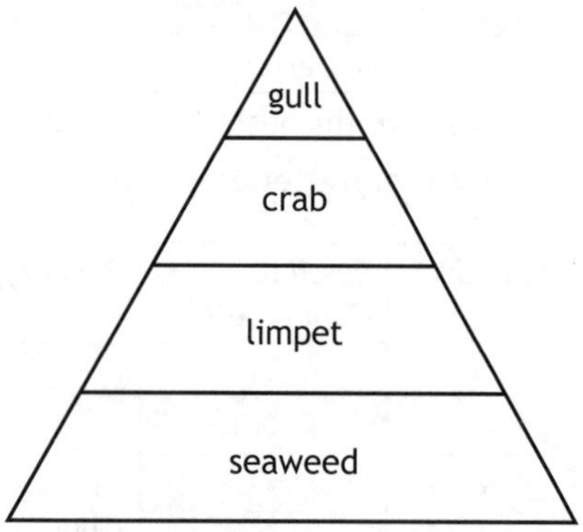

(b) (i) Flat (periwinkle)
Don't live on/occupy the same position on the shore/live on different/separate parts of the shore/small live at high tide and flat live at low tide/one lives at low tide and one at high tide

(ii) They are different species/they are not the same species/more than one species are competing

12. (a) (i) 2

(ii) **Increased** competition from Meadow grass or appropriate description of the increased competition eg less space for Ragwort to grow

(b) Sampling Technique: Pitfall trap **(1)**
Source of error:
Traps left too long/not checked regularly
Too high above soil surface/too low below soil surface/not level with soil surface
Not camouflaged
Too shallow
No drainage holes **(any one - 1)**

(c) Go to 3 **(1)**
Buttercup **(1)**
Pink campion **(1)**

13. (a) Mutation

(b) (i) Different numbers released/marked/captured
OR
To compare results

(ii) Fewer were eaten (by predators/birds)/better camouflaged so not eaten/camouflaged from predators/birds less likely to be eaten/seen by predators or birds/more dark moths eaten by predators or birds

(Answer must have reference to 'being eaten' or 'predators/birds')

(iii) Natural selection/survival of the fittest

14. (a) (i) When predators are present (the number of red spider) mites decrease/there are more (red spider) mites when there is no predator or converse

(ii) To allow it to be compared to the one with the predator/to compare the number of (red spider) mites with and without the predator/to show any difference is due to the predator

(b) <u>Biological control</u>

NATIONAL 5 BIOLOGY 2017

SECTION 1

Question	Response
1.	B
2.	D
3.	A
4.	B
5.	B
6.	B
7.	D
8.	C
9.	D
10.	A
11.	A
12.	C
13.	B
14.	A
15.	C
16.	C
17.	D
18.	C
19.	B
20.	C

SECTION 2

1. (a) (i) Cytoplasm – site of (chemical) reactions
OR
Cell membrane – controls/allows/lets entry and/or exit/passage of materials/substances/molecules
OR
Controls what enters/exits
OR
Nucleus – controls (all) cell activity/activities

(ii) Osmosis

(b) Cell wall

2. (a) (i) 3 Pairs of chromatids are pulled apart

(ii) Spindle (fibre)

(b) 40

3. (a) 1 = cytosine
2 = thymine

(b) Sequence/order of bases

(c) Messenger RNA/mRNA/MRNA

4. (a) Appropriate scale and label **(1)**
Scale must have 0, 108 or 120 and one other number in between
Label – Time (taken) for disc(s) to return to (the) surface s/seconds
Bars correctly plotted **(1)**

(b) Liver has the highest catalase activity/apple has the lowest catalase activity/different tissues have different catalase activity/animal tissue has higher catalase activity (than plants) or other appropriate conclusion

(c) Decrease

5. (a) (i) 1·3

(ii) Temperature

(iii) (Respiration is) controlled by enzymes/enzymes are needed **(1)**
Enzymes have been denatured (at 60°C) or description of denatured **(1)**

(iv) To show it is the **germinating/live** peas that are producing the result/using oxygen/respiring
OR
To show that <u>dead</u> peas do not respire

(b) X – Pyruvate
OR
Y – Ethanol/alcohol

6. (a) Discrete **(1)**
Heterozygous **(1)**

(b) (i) Testis/testes

(ii) Sperm <u>nucleus</u> and egg <u>nucleus</u> fuse or join together/sperm and egg <u>nuclei</u> fuse/gamete <u>nuclei</u> fuse or join together

(iii) Haploid cell or egg has half the number of chromosomes
OR
Diploid cell or zygote has double/twice the number of chromosomes
OR
Haploid cell or egg has one set of chromosomes/23 chromosomes whereas diploid cell or zygote has two sets of chromosomes/46 chromosomes

7. (a) 11:7

(b) (i) Oxygen/nutrients/glucose/amino acids

(ii) Reduce/stop smoking
Reduce fat in diet/cholesterol in diet/salt intake/sugar intake/alcohol intake/stress
Lose weight/healthier diet/healthier eating

(c) (Large) surface area/(rich) blood supply/(dense) capillary network

8. (a) 150

(b) (i) Will be less evaporation/water loss
OR
Plant will not require as much water

(ii) Dry

9. (a) Cerebellum

(b) 1. Detected by <u>receptors</u> **(1)**

2. Sent by <u>electrical</u> impulse/signal **(1)**

3. (Message/information/impulse goes) from sensory to relay neuron/
sensory ⟶ relay neuron **(1)**

4. Across synapse
OR
Chemical transfer between neurons **(1)**

10. (a) (i) Pancreas

(ii) Glucose is needed to release/give out energy
OR
If cells do not have glucose they release/give out less/no energy

(b) (i) S

(ii) P

(c) Receptor (protein)

11. (a) Set up more than one field for each variety/
Repeat the (whole) investigation/
Use more potatoes/plants in each field

(b) 175

(c) Number of potatoes/plants
Spacing between potatoes/plants
pH of soil
Nutrient content of soil
Moisture content of soil
Fertility of soil
Type of soil

(d) Pesticides/insecticides/predator/biological control/crop rotation

12. (a) Niche

(b) Mutation

(c) (Offspring would be) infertile/sterile

13.

Statement	*True*	*False*	*Correction*
Genetic variation within a population allows the population to adapt in a changing environment.	✓		
Isolation barriers can be geographical, environmental or reproductive.		✓	Ecological
Sub-populations evolve until they become genetically identical.		✓	Non-identical/varied/different

14. (a) (i) Nitrites

(ii) 3
OR
4

(b) (i) Plants/producers/denitrifying bacteria

(ii) To make protein/amino acids

(c) Fungi

15. (a) (i) Has most crusty lichen and these are common/found in high pollution

(ii) 6

(b) Indicator (species)

NATIONAL 5 BIOLOGY 2017 SPECIMEN QUESTION PAPER

SECTION 1

Question	Answer
1.	B
2.	D
3.	A
4.	A
5.	C
6.	B
7.	D
8.	C
9.	B
10.	C
11.	A
12.	D
13.	A
14.	D
15.	A
16.	B
17.	C
18.	A
19.	D
20.	B
21.	B
22.	D
23.	C
24.	B
25.	C

SECTION 2

1. (a) Y

(b) Large number of mitochondria present

(c) Chloroplasts present **(1)**

Contain chlorophyll/green pigment/are green **(1)**

2. (a) (i) From cell of alveolus wall to cell of capillary wall to red blood cell

(ii) (Oxygen) moves from a higher concentration to a lower concentration or down a concentration gradient

(b) There is no concentration gradient/difference in concentration/concentration equal in all cells

3. (a) (i) mRNA/messenger RNA

(ii) Bases **(1)**
C **(1)**

(b) Gene

(c) Different sequence/order of bases

4. (a) (i) Arginine

(ii) Lysine

(iii) Serine

(b) 1:3

(c) Appropriate scale – must have 0, 6.4, 7 or 8 and at least one other number in between **(1)**

Bars correctly plotted with clear bar tops **(1)**

5. (a) Carbon dioxide

(b) pH 5 **(1)**

Highest (average) number of bubbles (for most groups) **(1)**

(c) All flasks at same pH **(1)**

Any one from:
Yeast – different types of yeast in each flask
OR
Temperature – different temperatures
OR
Glucose – different glucose concentrations used **(1)**

6. (a) B A C E (D)

All required to be correct

(b) (Pairs of) chromatids/chromosomes line up at equator/centre (of the cell)

(Must have reference to what lines up and where)

(c) To maintain the (diploid) chromosome complement/so no genetic information is lost/so the daughter/new cells contain the same genetic information as the original cell

(d) 7

7. (a) (i) Target cell has complementary receptor (proteins) for the hormone/the hormone fits the receptor (proteins) on the target cells only/the hormone and receptor (proteins) have complementary shapes

(ii) Any one difference:

Hormone message – chemical/long-lasting/carried in blood/carried all over body
Nerve message – electrical/short-lived effect/carried along specific nerves/path

(Must be comparative between hormone and nerve)

(b) (i) Type 1

Insulin not produced

(Both parts needed)

(ii) Would stay higher than normal/would stay too high

(iii) Pancreas

8. (a) Heterozygous

(b)

	H	h
H	**HH**	**Hh**
h	**Hh**	**hh**

(All parts must be correct)

(c) HH and Hh

(Both are needed)

9. (a) To prevent water evaporating/being lost from the soil (which will affect the weight/mass)

(b) 1·41

(c) Exactly the same set up but without the plant

(d) Decrease

(e) Stomata/stoma

10. (a) Choose any two of arteries, veins and capillaries

Comparison of:
Thickness of walls
Muscularity of walls
Presence and absence of valves
Size of channel for blood flow

Any three for 3 marks

(Must compare chosen blood vessels and refer to structural differences)

(b) Carries oxygen

11. (a) (i) Mouths are all different shapes/sizes/structures

(ii) A, B, D (any two)

(b) Niche

(c) (3)-1-5-4-2

(All required to be correct)

(d) All the organisms living in a particular area and the non-living components (with which they interact)

12. (a) (i) Hydrogen

(ii) Light energy is trapped by chlorophyll **(1)**

Light energy/it is converted into chemical energy in ATP **(1)**

(Energy stored in sugar can be used for) respiration/converted into cellulose or starch or any other correctly named substance/protein synthesis or cell division or any other named plant process **(1)**

(b) Light intensity **(1)**
Carbon dioxide concentration **(1)**

13. (a) To find out if drinking beetroot/nitrate-rich juice affects sprint **and** decision making performance

(Both parts needed)

(b) (sprint and decision making) performance

(c)

Sprint test/Activities	*Time/Timing* (seconds)
Sprint	10
Slow pedalling	80
Rest	30

Suitable headings with appropriate units **(1)**
All information given in columns of table **(1)**

(d) Drinking nitrate-rich (beetroot) juice gives an (3·5%) improvement in sprint performance **and** an (3%) increase in their speed of making decisions

(e) Only used males/too small a sample/only tested on people involved in two sports

14. (a) L

(b) Shows the total available energy of the living organisms/population at each stage/level in a food chain

(c) Heat/movement/undigested material

15. (a) Initial populations all had different starting sizes

(b) 4·3

(c) Starling and yellow wagtail

(Both needed)

16. (a) (As you move from sample site 1 to sample site 5,) the abundance of Yellow Iris increases/it increases

(b) Soil moisture

(c) Wipe/dry the probe between samples
OR
Probe at the same depth each time

17. (a) Long and thin **(1)**
Egg wrack **(1)**
Bladder wrack **(1)**

(b) Egg wrack has bladders present along its length whereas Bladder wrack's (bladders) are in pairs

(Comparison needed)

(c) Brown or no bladders

Acknowledgements

Permission has been sought from all relevant copyright holders and Hodder Gibson is grateful for the use of the following:

Image © Pan Stock/Shutterstock.com (2016 Section 2 page 19);
Image © HHelene/Shutterstock.com (2016 Section 2 page 24);
Image © Rahul Alvares/Shutterstock.com (2017 Section 2 page 22);
Image © Margarita Borodina/Shutterstock.com (2017 SQP Section 2 page 15);
Article is adapted from "Beetroot juice boosts your decision making," taken from 'The Herald', Saturday 19th September 2015 (2017 SQP Section 2 page 22);
Image © Elena Blokhina/Shutterstock.com (2017 SQP Section 2 page 26).